Japanese Arts of the Heian Period

ASIA HOUSE GALLERY, *New York City, October 5–December 17, 1967*

FOGG ART MUSEUM, *Harvard University, Cambridge, Massachusetts*

January 17–February 25, 1968

1b. OVERLEAF: *Portrait of Shōtoku Taishi. Late 11th c. Color on silk;* H. *50¾ inches. (Shown only at Asia House Gallery.)*

Japanese Arts of the Heian Period:

794–1185

John Rosenfield

THE ASIA SOCIETY, INC. · Distributed by Harry N. Abrams, Inc.

Japanese Arts of the Heian Period: 794–1185 is the catalogue of an exhibition
selected by John Rosenfield, Associate Professor, Department of Fine Arts,
Harvard University, and shown in Asia House Gallery
in the autumn of 1967 as an activity of The Asia Society, to further
greater understanding and mutual appreciation between
the United States and the peoples of Asia.

An Asia House Gallery Publication

Printed in Japan

Library of Congress Catalogue Card Number: 67-22187

Additions to the Exhibition

A. BONTEN
Wood with traces of gesso; H. 40 inches (101.0 cm.)
Late 9th–early 10th century
The Art Museum, Princeton University

Images of Indra and Brahma, two deities symbolic of Hindu creeds, were often placed among sets of Buddhist images to demonstrate the inclusive and superior nature of the Buddhist faith. This powerful, massively carved statue of Brahma (Bonten) dates from a time when the native Japanese feeling and respect for wood conduced the sculptors to express freely the solidity and bulk of the material. The comma-shaped folds over the front of the skirt are merely light depressions in the integral mass of the form.

Published: Mayuyama, No. 23.

B. NYOIRIN KANNON
Ca. 900–950
Wood with coating of gesso and paint, and traces of gold; H. (figure) 23¾ inches (64.5 cm.)
Anonymous loan

This superb carving depicts an Esoteric form of the great Bodhisattva of Compassion, Kannon. The deity exists primarily to aid man in attaining prosperity and security in life as well as Supreme Enlightenment, the ultimate metaphysical reward of faith. Although most of the symbolic attributes of this sculpture have been lost, they would have enhanced this concept. Ordinarily the Nyoirin Kannon holds in its outer left hand the wheel that is the emblem of the Buddhist doctrine; in the inner right hand is the jewel which signifies the vast and precious treasure of the faith and also the capacity to achieve any goal. The outer right hand usually holds a rosary, and the middle right hand supports the head in a soft, pensive gesture signifying that the deity is making its vow to serve its devotees.

The oldest representation of this Bodhisattva in Japan dates from around A.D. 850 and is found in the ancient monastery of Kanshin-ji in the Kawachi district, a temple often visited by pilgrims heading toward Koyasan from the Osaka and Kyoto area (*Kokuhō*, Vol. II, pl. 25). The

Kanshin-ji figure, long treated as a "secret image" and rarely placed on view, has kept its surface coloring in almost perfect repair. The statue on display here is later than the Kanshin-ji piece by a half century or so, is smaller by twelve inches, and is considerably more sculpturesque. The atmosphere of sensuality and brooding introspection present in the Kanshin-ji work has been replaced here by a more genial and ebullient mood. These differences are symptomatic of the manner in which the extraordinarily tense, electric quality in early Japanese Esoteric Buddhist art was later softened and given a relaxed aspect.

C. SEATED MYŌ-Ō
Ca. 1000
Wood with coating of gesso and paint, and traces of gold; H. 15⅜ inches (39 cm.)
John G. Powers, New York

This remarkable work of Esoteric Buddhist sculpture may well have come from the northeast part of Honshu Island. It has a slightly rustic, provincial flavor in its assertive air and open countenance. Close similarities to the fleshiness of the cheeks and neck and the linear treatment of the garment folds may be found in sculptures from Iwate prefecture (Takeshi Kuno, *Nihon no Chōkoku* [Vol. I, Tōhoku], Tokyo, 1964, pls. 12, 13, 17). Carved from a single block of wood, the head and body are not deeply modeled in a sculpturesque manner, but are somewhat flattened and relief-like. The right foot, shown as though seen from above, is a touch of charming naiveté.

Generally speaking, when Tantric deities are shown with three heads they are ordinarily given more than two arms, as though to emphasize their superhuman powers. Instances do occur, however, in which Dai-itoku Myō-ō (or Yamāntaka, the Bright King who has vanquished death) is depicted in a manner similar to this figure (*Taishō Shinshū Daizōkyō Zuzō*, Tokyo, 1932, Vol. III, p. 876). It is, therefore, possible that this figure formed part of a set of the Five Bright Kings (Myō-ō) installed in a temple of the Tendai or Shingon sect in the remote Northeast.

NOTE: Because of its extremely fragile condition, number 2, Gōzanze Myō-ō, has been withdrawn from the exhibition.

Bonten. Late 9th–early 10th c. Wood with traces of gesso; H. *40 inches.*

Nyoirin Kannon. Ca. 900–950. Wood with coating of gesso and paint, and traces of gold; H. *(figure)* 23¾ *inches.*

Seated Myō-ō. Ca. 1000. Wood with coating of gesso and paint, and traces of gold; H. 15⅜ *inches.*

Contents

Acknowledgments

It is thanks to the generosity of the Lila Acheson Wallace Fund, Inc. that this special Heian exhibition at Asia House Gallery has been arranged. Its support has not only made it possible to borrow rare and fragile pieces from American private collections and museums but has assured our Japanese importations as well. The latter consist of works of major importance that have been sent from Japan through the assistance of the Japanese National Commission for the Protection of Cultural Properties. Listed as "National Treasures" are two rare eighth century portraits from the Ichijō-ji Temple, and of equal interest is an exquisite page of Heian calligraphy—a torn-paper work of surprisingly modern aspect. This was formerly housed in a Kyoto temple and is now the property of Mr. Saburo Hiraki of Tokyo. Mr. Matsuo Murayama, Secretary General, and Mr. Bunsaku Kurata and Mr. Takaaki Matsushita of the National Commission for the Protection of Cultural Properties were most helpful in arranging for these loans. The Asia Society is also indebted to the ever-kind assistance of the Kokusai Bunka Shinkokai (the Society for International Cultural Relations) which has expedited the arrangements.

This is the first exhibition of the treasures of Japan's Heian period (794–1185) ever to be presented in the West, a somewhat surprising fact in view of the importance of the epoch, which lasted nearly four hundred years. Professor John Rosenfield of Harvard University, the distinguished author of this catalogue, has been wholly responsible for the choice of objects displayed. Because his search for worthy material and his study of various pieces became a labor of love over a period of several years, Dr. Rosenfield was able to enlist the cooperation of the members of his graduate seminar in these investigations during the spring of 1966. Both the Asia House Gallery and Dr. Rosenfield are grateful to these students for their devoted assistance.

Dr. Rosenfield also joins with us in voicing a deep indebtedness to the following kind friends who have notably assisted us in the fulfillment of this project: Mr. Shoichi Uehara of the National Museum of Nara, Mr. Masaki Nakano of the Tokyo National Museum, the late Mr. Robert Treat Paine, Dr. Jan Fontein, Mr. Chimyo Horioka, Dr. and Mrs. Edwin Cranston, Miss Julia Meech, Mr. Money Hickman and Mr. Robin Berrington.

In addition to the above named friends and perhaps before all other contributors to this difficult undertaking, we wish to thank the owners of the Heian treasures that are here presented. Their generosity in making the loans has been prerequisite to the entire project. Because of their lively interest in the Heian exhibition, we are able to indicate the surprising richness of American holdings of this early Japanese period—an age that marks the true birth-date of Japan as a great and independent culture.

Gordon Bailey Washburn, *Director, Asia House Gallery*

Lenders

Museum of Fine Arts, Boston, Massachusetts
The Brooklyn Museum, New York
Mr. and Mrs. Jackson Burke, New York
The Cleveland Museum of Art, Cleveland, Ohio
M. H. De Young Memorial Museum, San Francisco, California
Mr. and Mrs. Solomon Diamond, Pasadena, California
Fogg Art Museum, Cambridge, Massachusetts
Capt. and Mrs. Roger Gerry, Roslyn, New York
Mr. and Mrs. Money Hickman, Cambridge, Massachusetts
Mr. Saburo Hiraki, Tokyo, Japan
Mr. Howard C. Hollis, New York
Honolulu Academy of Arts, Hawaii
The Ichijō-ji Monastery, Hyogo prefecture, Japan
University of Indiana Art Gallery, Bloomington, Indiana
Los Angeles County Museum of Art, Los Angeles, California
The Metropolitan Museum of Art, New York
University of Michigan Museum of Art, Ann Arbor, Michigan
Nelson Gallery—Atkins Museum, Kansas City, Missouri
The New York Public Library, New York
Peabody Museum, Salem, Massachusetts
Philadelphia Museum of Art, Philadelphia, Pennsylvania
Mr. John G. Powers, New York
The Art Museum, Princeton University, Princeton, New Jersey
Mr. and Mrs. John D. Rockefeller 3rd, New York
Seattle Art Museum, Seattle, Washington
Mr. Harold P. Stern, Washington, D.C.
The Worcester Art Museum, Worcester, Massachusetts

Introduction

11. OPPOSITE: *The Bodhisattva Nikkō. Early 9th c. Japanese yew wood;* H. *18⅜ inches. (Shown only at Asia House Gallery.)*

In the year 784 an order was given that a great city be built to provide a new setting for the Emperor of Japan and his court, the bureaus of the Imperial government, the proud aristocratic households, and the hosts of artisans and commoners who served them. After ten years of work at Nagaoka the capital was again moved,[1] and established finally on the verdant, well-watered plain near the foot of Mount Hiei, the site of the modern city of Kyoto. It was called the Heian Kyō, Capital of Peace and Tranquility, and for almost four hundred years this metropolis served as the focus of the artistic and cultural life of the Empire.

The courtiers of the city, guided by the Buddhist clergy, endowed the construction of temples and monasteries, and provided them with images and ritual implements whose elegance set the standard of Buddhist arts throughout the Empire. This same aristocracy also developed a distinctive etiquette, a way of life which has been aptly named "the rule of taste" by Sir George Sansom. With intense fervor they sought refinement of their esthetic sensibility, and they produced a native style of literature and narrative painting which are among the most moving expressions of the Japanese people —the *Tale of Genji* by the Lady Murasaki, for example, and the hand scrolls which illustrate it.

---

1. The Japanese were accustomed to frequent changes in the seat of government. Notions of the impurity of death had long prompted them to build a new Imperial Palace after an Emperor had died; and it was not until 710, when Nara was established, that they first set up a large-scale capital with an air of permanence.

These four hundred years are often called the Heian period, because the capital which gave the era its name was indeed the center of the important forms of authority in Japan—political, economic, religious, and artistic. Nevertheless, none of these forms continued in a steady, unbroken pattern throughout the entire span of time. For the visual arts, it would be far more appropriate to think of the Heian period as a sequence of creative outbursts, unevenly spaced in time, often loosely connected with one another and arising from particular, local contexts.

The entire notion of periods as "distinguishable portions of history" has been seriously criticized in recent decades for being a purely academic concept, an artificial division of cultural matters which took place in an unbroken continuum of time. Certainly we cannot detect a single unifying spirit in all Japanese art during the Heian period. For any given decade we are confronted with a bewildering variety of works representing different strands of the cultural fabric. Some works were made for religious movements that were vitalized by an atmosphere of strong faith, while others belonged to relatively inactive sects which had lost some of their confidence or élan. There are objects which were affected by the sumptuous arts of China, and those that reflect austere native Japanese canons of taste; there are objects which were made in or near the capital city by craftsmen of the highest skill and even genius, and others made in the remote provinces by men whose very clumsiness imbued their work with an amiable flavor.

The Heian Capital.
Solid lines are the plan of the ancient city. Broken lines are the streets of the modern Kyoto.

A. Imperial Palace compound. Original site
B. Sujaku-ōji. Main North-South boulevard
C. Tōji
D. Site of Saiji
E. Site of the Rashōmon
F. Imperial Palace compound. Current location
G. Approximate location of Michinaga's Hōjō-ji
H. (Nishi) Hongan-ji
I. Sanjūsangen-dō, or the Renge-ō-in

J. Rokuhara district. Site of Taira Kiyomori's villa
K. Approximate location of Shirakawa's Hō-shō-ji
L. Kamo River
M. To Mount Hiei
N. Katsura River
O. Kōryū-ji
P. To Jingo-ji and Kōzan-ji
Q. To Uji and the Byōdō-in

Moreover, the four-hundred-year period seems to be sharply divisible in the middle, roughly around the 970's or 980's. By that time, the architecture and imagery of the Esoteric Buddhist sects were being replaced by those of the Pure Land creeds[2] as prime objects of patronage; the Fujiwara family had approached its apogee of power and influence; the Heian aristocracy had developed a brilliant court literature, highly original forms of calligraphy, and narrative painting—each of them free from obvious Chinese influences. The esthetic tenor of the latter half of the period differs markedly from that of the first—lighter, less intellectual and ponderous, far more Japanese in spirit.

If we bear these reservations in mind, we may still recognize in a "Heian period" a useful concept for the history of art, if only because the conditions of patronage and the moods of expression changed so rapidly at both its beginning and its end. The end of the Heian period was marked by thirty years of violent civil war between martial clans contending for the right to replace the Fujiwaras as the dominant power in the civil government. In 1185 military forces, chiefly from Eastern Japan and led by Minamoto no Yoritomo, established a *de facto* military government at Kamakura; and a new kind of political authority, basically feudal in nature and reinforced by the might of arms, replaced the more indirect and subtle forms of domination exerted by the Fujiwaras.

The ending of the Heian period also marked the

─────────
2. See page 30.

close of a much longer historical epoch which the Japanese call their Kodai, or Ancient Era. It began in the mid-sixth century with the importation of Buddhism and of Chinese modes of government. During this entire time, the artistic gifts of the Japanese people were channeled primarily into religious symbolism, and within the narrow restrictions of traditional Buddhist icons a surprising range of emotional expression was possible. The highest levels of artistic insight were imbued with spiritual exaltation such as that experienced by the great monks; but heroic, tender, and intimate moods, pathos, and even coarse humor were also conveyed.

Throughout the twelfth century, however, such secular forms of art as narrative and landscape painting, pure decoration, fine calligraphy, and state portraiture gained increasing freedom from the criteria of traditional Buddhist imagery. By the end of the thirteenth century, the breakdown of creativity within hieratic Buddhist arts was more or less complete, despite the brilliant revival of temple sculpture in the Nara workshops of Kaikei, Unkei, and their followers. Moreover, the rise of the Zen sect to prominence in Kamakura and Kyoto in the thirteenth century brought a radically different, naturalistic esthetic system, based in part on Chinese-style ink painting and the kind of sensibility cultivated in the tea ceremony. Thus the Heian period encompassed the mature, late phases of traditional Buddhist arts, their decline in originality and expressive power, and the first harbingers of the new esthetic order of the Japanese Middle Ages.

American collectors, surprisingly active in this difficult field of connoisseurship, have generously agreed to share their works for this exhibition. Some pieces are comparable in quality to any which have been preserved in Japan, but certain aspects of Heian art are not available to us: for example, giant hanging scroll paintings such as the Raikō and Nirvāna scenes of Kōyasan; rare narrative scroll paintings, among them the *Genji Monogatari Emaki* and the *Shigisan Engi*; or monumentally conceived, solid wood images of Shinto deities. Nevertheless, we enjoy a very rich selection of material, and even though these objects have been removed from their original settings, they can prepare us for the ultimate experience of Japanese art in its homeland.

The Esoteric Buddhist Arts

5b. OPPOSITE: *Page from a Notebook Depicting the Kongōkai Mandala; Kongōke Bosatsu. Attributed to Takuma Tametō (active mid-12th c.). Ink and color on paper;* H. *(originally)* 9¹⁵⁄₁₆ *inches.*

16

The Heian period began on a note of reform. The capital had been moved from Nara to Heian Kyō largely in order to free the Imperial throne from the excessive influence of the Buddhist clergy. The Emperor Shōmu (701–756) had virtually bankrupted the government in his ambitious project to construct and house the giant bronze image of the Buddha Dainichi at Tōdai-ji in Nara, the chief official monastery of the nation. So great had been the religious fervor of the Imperial Household in Nara that Shōmu's daughter, the Empress Kōken (733–770) who succeeded him, tried to abdicate the throne in favor of a Buddhist monk and thereby to convert Japan into a virtually theocratic state. Conservative courtiers resisted this effort, and finally prevailed upon the successors of Kōken to move the capital out from under the shadow of these powerful Nara temples. This is not to say that the courtiers were anti-Buddhist, but only that they wished to preserve the traditions of the monarchy from the encroachment of religious power.

When the new Heian capital was planned only two major temples were established within the city limits, Tōji (the Eastern Temple), which still stands, and Saiji (the Western Temple), which rapidly declined. Like guardians, they were placed just behind the Rashōmon Gate at the south entrance to the city, on either side of the boulevard which divided the city into halves. At the northern end of the boulevard was the Imperial Palace compound, the city itself being laid out in the symmetrical, checkerboard pattern which had been adapted from Chinese city planning.

Coincidental with the opening of the new capital was the return to Japan of two monks, Saichō, who arrived in 805, and Kūkai, who returned in 807. These brilliant young men had gone to China and studied the doctrines of Esoteric Buddhism, sometimes called Vajrayāna ("The Thunderbolt Vehicle") or Buddhist Tantrism. This powerful ideology had been formulated in India in the eighth century A.D. and missionaries carried it to Central Asia, Tibet, and China, as well as to Java and Cambodia. It spread with great speed, for its doctrines offered immense rewards not only in the spiritual world, where the attainment of enlightenment could be hastened by the use of rituals and charms, but also in material realms—personal safety or prosperity.

Esoteric Buddhism had begun to take hold in Japan during the Nara period, especially in the worship of Dainichi and such Tantric forms of Avalokiteśvara as the Thousand-armed Kannon. But the doctrines brought back by Saichō and Kūkai placed Dainichi in a far more inclusive and systematic theology populated with a huge pantheon. Many of these gods, moreover, had been only recently conceived and were strongly tinged with Hindu notions of divine power and energy. The new dogma deeply impressed the aristocracy of the Heian capital, who encouraged Saichō and Kūkai at the expense of the religious circles of Nara. Of equal importance were the liturgical aspects of the new creed (for example the Goma ceremony in which piles of wooden slats inscribed with prayers were burned at a high altar; the system of complex

OPPOSITE: *Fig. 1. Jikoku-ten in the Lecture Hall of Tōji, Kyoto.*

hand gestures [*mudrās*] used in prayer; the recitation of Sanskrit magical formulae [*mantras*]; and a dramatic baptismal ritual) and the esthetic appurtenances such as the complex bronze altar furnishings, which must have looked like machines for invoking the powerful energies of the pantheon.

Saichō, before going to China, had founded a small hermitage at Enryaku-ji atop Mount Hieizan, only a few miles northeast of the capital. After his return he converted it into an immense sanctuary whose halls were scattered over the wooded summit and ravines. Enryaku-ji became the headquarters of the Japanese branch of the Tendai sect, originally founded in China in the sixth century on Mount T'ien-t'ai in Che-chiang. This school had aimed at unifying the various doctrines and creeds within Buddhism into a "single Vehicle," but in the eighth century its outlook was strongly colored by Esoterism.

Kūkai built a similar hermitage atop Mount Kōya, in the wildly rugged, isolated peaks of the Kii country some fifty miles from the capital. This became the headquarters in Japan of the Shingon sect, one which was entirely Tantric in its ideology. Kūkai was also given authority over Tōdai-ji in Nara, and was made Abbot of the Kyoto monastery of Tōji.

The visual arts were of great importance to Kūkai, who had an impact upon the history of Japanese art which has never been completely measured. He prescribed, for example, the installation of twenty-one large statues in the Lecture Hall of Tōji, to serve as the focus of a ceremony designed to protect the welfare of the Empire. Despite some latter-day replacements, this set of images remains one of the most powerful expressions of the Tantric ethos in Japan. In 806, Kūkai wrote the following statement concerning the vital role of the arts in the scale of values of Esoteric Buddhism:

The law (*dharma*) has no speech, but without speech it cannot be expressed. Eternal truth (*tathatā*) transcends color, but only by means of color can it be understood. Mistakes will be made in the effort to point at the truth, for there is no clearly defined method of teaching, but even when art does not excite admiration by its unusual quality, it is a treasure which protects the country and benefits the people.

In truth, the esoteric doctrines are so profound as to defy their enunciation in writing. With the help of painting, however, their obscurities may be understood. The various attitudes and *mudrās* of the holy images all have their source in Buddha's love, and one may attain Buddhahood at sight of them. Thus the secrets of the sutras and the commentaries can be depicted in art, and the essential truths of the esoteric teaching are all set forth therein. Neither teachers nor students can dispense with it. Art is what reveals to us the state of perfection.[1]

Esoteric Buddhism, which in Japanese is called Mikkyō, wrought numerous changes in the artistic atmosphere of Japan. Most obvious was the sense of fiery energy in several classes of Tantric images, such as the Myō-ō (Bright Kings), whose multiple heads and arms clearly reflected their Indian origin. Other early Tantric statues have a strange sensuality about them, as in the Nyoirin Kannon of the Kanshin-ji temple, in which an almost feminine

1. *Memorial on the Presentation of the List of Newly Imported Sūtras*; quoted in de Bary (editor), *Sources of Japanese Tradition*, New York, 1958, pp. 141, 142.

aura permeates an image which is supposed, theologically, to be without gender.

The great numbers and sheer complexity of the pantheon were other characteristics of Esoterism, evidence of its profundity and universality. The Mikkyō sects made prominent use of mandalas, schematic diagrams in which each deity was assigned a place in the hieratic pattern. Large painted mandalas were hung in the main image halls, serving as the focal points of rituals. Novice monks were obliged to meditate on them, to memorize the spiritual significance of each of the components, and to identify the distinguishing gestures and ritual implements of each deity.

During the Heian period, the Buddhist faith spread more deeply than before into the remote parts of the Empire. In certain isolated regions, particularly the far northeast, a strongly regional flavor began to appear in the arts, and rather primitive imagery was produced in large quantities by monks with little artistic training. These provincial deviations from metropolitan standards of form, which are often so charmingly simple, are a striking feature of the arts of the Heian period.

Esoterism remained the dominant force in Japanese Buddhist art from around 800 to 950. By the latter half of the tenth century, however, much of the heroic fervor of the new doctrine had abated. Attempts were made to harmonize it with Pure Land Buddhism; tranquility and equipoise returned even to the wrathful images, and its art forms became rather stereotyped. To be sure, Tantric Buddhism has remained vital in Japan to this day. While it no longer seems highly relevant to the life of a modern, industrialized nation it still exerts an appeal, and has preserved intact ancient liturgy and symbolism which, in China, were supplanted by Tibetan Lamaism, a newer and even more demonic form of Esoterism.

The Classic Buddhist Tradition

15. OPPOSITE: *Flying Angel. Second half of the 11th c. Wood with traces of gesso and gold;* H. 33½ *inches.*

Amid the often baffling diversity which appears in so much of the history of Japanese art, one major thread of continuity may be traced throughout the evolution of religious painting and sculpture. This tradition was based on the great international style of East Asian Buddhist imagery, which reached its maturity during the early eighth century in T'ang China and remained a strong influence in Japan through the thirteenth century.

The canons of beauty which governed this mode were essentially of Indian origin, most eloquently realized in the carvings of Sārnāth and Mathurā of the later fifth and sixth centuries and in some of the Ajantā wall paintings. But a marked East Asian flavor appeared as this style was adopted in such metropolitan Chinese centers as Ch'ang-an and Lo-yang, and as it spread to Korea and Japan. The best Japanese representatives of the style are the bronze images belonging to the temple of Yakushi-ji in Nara—the giant trinity in the Kondō and the Shō Kannon—or the wall paintings of the Kondō of Hōryū-ji which were lost by fire in 1949.

We call this style "classic" because of its high artistic quality, its universality, its atmosphere of calmness and repose. Even though its guardian deities may be menacing, the predominant mood is not the demonic *terribilità* or introspective mysticism of Mikkyō but rather an air of grandeur and serenity. Actually the classic imagery is as hieratic and impersonal as that of the Byzantine Church, but its formal qualities are closely attuned to the dominant spiritual ideals of Mahāyāna Buddhism. The entire system, moreover, is centered about one

basic icon type, the image of a fully illumined sage —a Buddha or Tathāgata (Nyorai)—dressed in a monastic robe without ornaments, seated in meditation or else offering instruction or benediction, his face at once ideally perfect and imbued with humanity and compassion. Equally prominent, however, are the Bodhisattvas, the active agents of the compassion of the Tathāgatas. Their youthful bodies adorned with jewels and garlands, they are ethereal beings, personifications of immaterial conceptions such as wisdom, compassion, and grace.

At the dawn of the Heian period, however, such classical Buddhist forms had become old-fashioned, for the special iconographic demands of Esoterism had been felt as early as the mid-eighth century. In addition a kind of self-conscious primitivism swept through some of the Nara sculpture workshops during the last three decades of the century. The same mood seems to have affected the Chinese; perhaps there had been a surfeit of the qualities of effortless grace and beauty, for carvings produced in both Ch'ang-an and Nara were given a somber, brooding power, their faces full and almost scowling, their bodies stocky and muscular. In Japan the favored material was wood, solid logs of cedar or cypress impressive for their sheer bulk, rather than the more malleable media of clay, lacquer, or bronze, which lent themselves to subtle surface effects. The most familiar examples of this austere, anti-classical taste are the statues of Yakushi (the Healing Buddha) dating from the 780's and '90's and the seated Buddha of Murō-ji. The taste for these aggressively heavy forms lasted well beyond

OPPOSITE: *Fig. 2. Seated Buddha. Murō-ji, Nara prefecture.*

the Jōgan regnal era (859–876), but the style is often given the name Jōgan.

Despite these developments, the classical spirit was not forgotten in the early decades of the Heian period and some exceedingly elegant unpainted wood images of the Eleven-headed Kannon were created in this manner early in the ninth century. They are found today at such temples as Hokke-ji in Nara and Kōgen-ji along the east shore of Lake Biwa. In fact, the classical style remained a kind of common denominator of almost all Buddhist art of this period, even where its gracefulness was counterbalanced by Esoteric ferocity. Around the beginning of the eleventh century, as the special flavor of Mikkyō images began to fade along with the preference for the "Jōgan" style, the classic manner again emerged as the leading artistic system for Buddhist imagery.

It is a fascinating exercise in stylistic analysis to assemble dated statues of standard iconographic types, such as the guardian figures or seated Buddhas, and to trace the evolution of these types decade by decade through the four centuries of the Heian period. Despite short-term deviations, rather consistent technical and stylistic changes took place. They were analogous, in a sense, to the transitions of European sculpture from the Renaissance to the Rococo periods, but Japanese sculptors, working for the Buddhist faith, had quite different conceptions of the world of nature from those of Europeans. Even though Japanese sculpture evolved in a "lawful" manner, it was not according to the laws of Wölfflin.

Among the changes which can be outlined in very general terms was the abandonment of solid wood sculpture in favor of hollow figures made of many thin-carved sections of wood, carefully assembled and glued and pegged together. The sense of ponderous, solid bulk and deep three-dimensionality gave way to delicacy and to a mathematical precision in surface effects. Similarly, the deeply undercut garment folds with their complicated rhythms were replaced by an almost linear arrangement of flattened pleats. Mass production deprived statues of a certain sense of uniqueness and intensity of expression. The guardian figures became more amiable and less threatening in character. Centuries of accumulated experience in the sculpture workshops gave rise to a virtuosity in the handling of plaster and lacquer surfaces which approaches realism.

Because of their fragility, it is more difficult to assemble enough dated examples of painting to document their development in the same detail as sculpture. It is evident, however, that by the middle of the twelfth century the conservative classical style had been suffused by an atmosphere of dematerialized form. In small, votive, hanging scrolls such as the celebrated Shaka of Jingo-ji, delicate decorative effects play over the surface—in the filigree design of the halo and in the embroidery on the Buddha's robe, where circular patterns cross arbitrarily over the lines of the legs as though to deny the physical actuality of the Buddha himself. Some writers charge this kind of painting with having lost its religious power and having become

OPPOSITE: *Fig. 3. Eleven-headed Kannon. Kōgen-ji, Shiga prefecture.*

merely an adjunct of the luxury arts of the aristocracy. Moreover, it is evident that, by the end of the Heian period, stylistically the arts of the court had markedly influenced those of the monasteries; but a strong religious feeling endures in these paintings. The colors are muted, the designs evoke a divine presence—a quiet, enraptured vision of deities who had become the vehicles of purest grace and compassionate power.

The Arts of the Pure Land Creed

OPPOSITE: *Fig. 5. Phoenix Hall, Byōdō-in. Uji, near Kyoto.*

By the year 1000, the citizens of the Heian capital felt the full effects of a new current of religious enthusiasm generated by monks who preached doctrines of salvation through the worship of the Buddha Amida. The most influential voice was that of Genshin (942–1017), who resided on Mount Hiei. Genshin circulated treatises which stressed that the compassion of Amida was so pervasive that a man need only invoke the Buddha's name with a sincere heart (*nembutsu*) in order to receive divine assistance. Upon death the believer would be reborn in a Pure Land, the Western Paradise of Amida, where he would escape from the cycle of birth and death simply by dwelling in the purity and beauty of heaven and hearing the Buddha's instruction.

Although these ideas were quite ancient, dating back to the first century A.D. in India and the early versions of the Lotus Sūtra (the *Saddharma-pundarīka* or *Hokke-kyō*), a strange combination of circumstances caused their sudden rise to popularity in the eleventh century. One factor must have been the potent idea of the Mappō (the End of the Law), a Buddhist version of an ancient Indian concept that human society must pass through an unending cycle of rise, decline, fall, and then revival. Some 1500 years after the death of Śākyamuni (the Buddha), mankind was thought to be entering a final stage in the decline of human virtue and ability to understand the Buddhist Law. According to one Japanese account, this period would begin precisely in A.D. 1052, and by the time its end was reached the faith would have entirely disappeared

from the earth. It would revive again, however, and virtue reappear among men; then Maitreya, the Buddha of the Future, would descend from Paradise to preach the Law as the cycle began once more.

The mighty Fujiwara Michinaga, early in his life, played a prominent role in the custom of interring large deposits of religious objects in order to preserve them until the coming of Maitreya. Called Kyōzuka or Sutra Mounds, these deposits have come to light throughout Japan, yielding religious texts written on gilded bronze plates, tiles, or paper. Bronze mirrors were also included as personal *ex voto* donations, along with altar equipment and bronze statues. The richest of all the Sutra Mounds is on Mount Kimpu, in the Yoshino district, popularly believed to be the place of Maitreya's return to earth, and there, in 1007, Michinaga buried a set of fifteen sutra scrolls copied in his own hand.

It was believed as well that in the Degenerate Latter Days of the Law man could be saved only by a divine force greater than himself, the compassion of Amida. And thus the wealthy families of the capital region and the provinces began to build Amida Halls to enshrine images of the Buddha, along with scenes of his Paradise and of the Amida Raikō, his descent amid a heavenly entourage of musicians and Bodhisattvas to receive the souls of the dying. One of the most elaborate of all Amida Halls must have been the one built by Michinaga in 1020. Erected within the compound of his personal temple, the giant Hōjō-ji which has totally disappeared, it enshrined nine Amida figures. These

OPPOSITE: *Fig. 6. Seated Amitābha, by Jōchō. Phoenix Hall, Byōdō-in. Uji.*

images symbolized the belief that the Western Paradise itself was divided into nine levels in order to accommodate the different degrees of virtue among men. Michinaga is said to have died before an image of Amida, holding a golden cord tied to the deity's hands, the *nembutsu* on his lips, and surrounded by monks chanting the *Hokke-kyō* to insure his rebirth in Paradise.

A substantial number of these Amida Halls have survived, the best known and most accessible being the Phoenix Hall of the Byōdō-in at Uji, southeast of Kyoto. It was built in 1052 by Michinaga's son, Fujiwara Yorimichi, head of the Fujiwara clan and Chancellor of State. Set before a small pond which was excavated in the shape of the Sanskrit letter A, the Phoenix Hall must have been conceived as a large-scale model of Amida's heavenly palace. Not more than three miles away is a more modest Amida Hall belonging to Hokkai-ji, a small temple which was once the country villa of the powerful Hino family, aristocrats of high standing in the government. And at Hiraizumi in the far northeast, the local rulers built, in 1124, an Amida Hall called the Konjiki-dō, at their family tutelary temple, Chūson-ji. Beneath a tripartite altar and three images of Amida were placed the actual remains of three successive leaders of the clan.

The ideals of the Pure Land creed had a singular effect on the arts and architecture, for they gave rise to an atmosphere of visionary and ethereal forms. The main rewards of this faith were to come in the afterlife, and not in this world as the Mikkyō systems propounded. Hence the function of temple architecture and imagery was to suggest the idyllic beauty of Paradise and the radiance and effortless motion of the great deities.

The sheer quantity of images commissioned in the eleventh and twelfth centuries is difficult to imagine. In both the Heian capital and in Nara, the old "Southern Capital," halls were built to enshrine one thousand statues of Kannon. Wealthy families donated sets of Buddhist scriptures running to hundreds of scrolls, illuminated and written by hand. Michinaga built his vast temple, the Hōjō-ji; around 1077 the Emperor Shirakawa commissioned an equally elaborate Hōshō-ji, with a full panoply of special halls and cult images; his successor the Emperor Horikawa dedicated his Sonshō-ji in 1102. The Sonshō-ji was equipped with a Kondō, a Lecture Hall, a Baptistry, Yakushi-dō, Mandala Hall, Hall for the Five Myō-ō, one for Kannon, two Pagodas, and a great hall with nine images of Amida. The next Emperor, Uda, built his temple, the Saishō-ji, in 1118, and this cycle continued until the mid-century wars between the Fujiwaras, Tairas, and Minamotos brought an end to such benefactions.

The influences of increased patronage were felt above all in the sculpture workshops, which were forced to devise assembly line techniques to meet the demand for images. The system is thought to have been devised by Jōchō. Trained by his father on the projects for Michinaga's Hōjō-ji, Jōchō became the most esteemed master of his day, and organized a private sculpture workshop in the capital city where he perfected the process of assembled wood-block construction. He employed dozens of pieces of thin wood, pegged and glued together, to build statues eight feet high that were relatively light in weight and safe from the deep cracks which afflicted solid wood figures as they dried out.

Jōchō's large Amida figure created in 1053 for the Phoenix Hall of the Byōdō-in is the chief sculptural landmark of its era. A mathematically precise and yet humane image, its body is taut with a kind of inner pneumatic tension, and the folds of the garment are carved in shallow relief. This master sculptor's methods were gradually standardized by his successors into rather bland, if charming, formulae and spread throughout the Empire; but it was not until the last quarter of the twelfth century, with the appearance in Nara of men with the genius of Kōkei and his son, Unkei, that Buddhist sculpture re-established for a brief period its wide emotional range and originality.

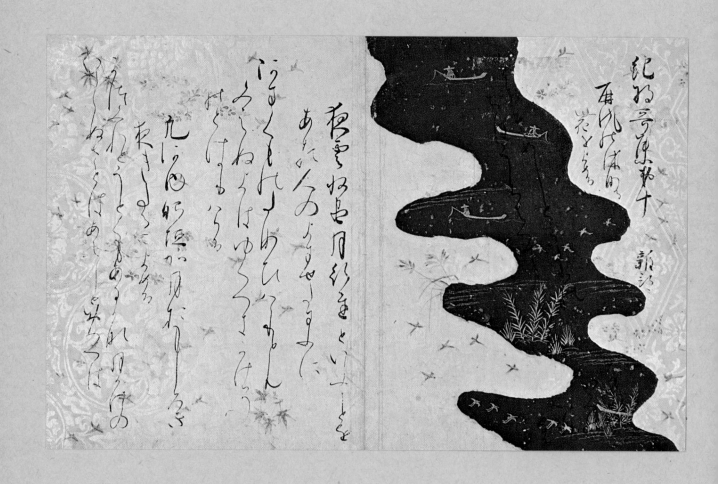

The Arts of the Court

37a. OPPOSITE: *Double page from the Collected Poems of Tsurayuki. Early 12th c. Ink on ornamented paper; H.* 7^{15}⁄$_{16}$ *inches (approx.). (Shown only at Asia House Gallery.)*

The laws of chance which govern the survival of fragile objects have ordained that, with a few exceptions, the oldest existing examples of Heian lacquer, narrative scroll painting, and textiles—the sumptuous, courtly arts—are those of the twelfth century. Even these are rare, and few have left Japan. Moreover, the surviving objects may be likened to planets which reflect the light of a sun no longer visible to us, for they were the later products of a movement which had gained its main direction during the lifetime of Michinaga, a century earlier.

A lively account of the passion for courtly arts among the Heian aristocracy of the day may be gleaned from the *Tale of Genji*, written by Murasaki Shikibu, Lady-in-Waiting to Michinaga's daughter, the Empress Akiko. Amid the poignant, semi-fictional histories of affairs of the heart are descriptions of picture-judging sessions and debates on the nature of beauty held among the ladies and gentlemen of the court. The tale tells of the eagerness with which these courtiers collected Chinese and Japanese paintings, of their skill as amateur painters and calligraphers. The novel also describes the lacquered cosmetic boxes inlaid with mother-of-pearl designs bearing secret love poems, the rich brocade kimonos, and fine ink landscapes mounted on folding screens. The author remarks that this was a moment in the history of Japan when the whole energy of the nation seemed to be concentrated on a search for the loveliest method of mounting paper scrolls.

This climate of estheticism must have been similar in many ways to that which prevailed in the courts of the Chinese. The Emperor Hui-tsung, for example, before his downfall in 1127, had encouraged the growth of the Imperial Painting Academy, had patronized the finest pottery kilns, had gathered poets, archaeologists, and artists around him, had assembled a great collection of old pictures, and had himself practiced painting with serious dedication. A century and a half earlier in Nanking, capital of the Southern T'ang state, the Emperor Li Hou-chu had also bestowed great wealth and favors on the circle of poets, painters, and philosophers he had assembled. Surprisingly, strong stylistic affinities to tenth century court painting in Nanking (as we know it from works attributed to Ku Hung-chung or Chou Wen-chü) appear in the oldest illustrated versions of the *Tale of Genji*, painted ca. 1140. Needless to say, Japanese courtly arts possess their own distinctive flavor, but the taste of the aristocracy in China and Japan had many things in common. In the apartments of the Heian Imperial Palace, women read the tragic romance of the concubine Yang Kuei-fei and the T'ang Emperor Hsüan-tsung with as much emotion as did the ladies of K'ai-feng or Hang-chou.

The illustrated Genji scrolls may well have been made in the E-dokoro, the official painting atelier operated as part of the government bureacracy and housed in the palace compound. Romantic narrative paintings of this kind were done with intense colors and boldly abstract compositions, and yet they were imbued with the peculiar air of melancholy which is often found in the poetry and

OPPOSITE: *Fig. 7.* Tale of Genji, *Takewa Chapter. Detail of Prince Kaoru. Tokugawa Collection, Nagoya.*

prose of the Heian court. This was not the only style practiced in the E-dokoro, however. A more descriptive manner, characterized by thin washes of color and calligraphic outlines, was used for handscrolls depicting the great court ceremonies, rebellions, conspiracies, and miraculous events in the capital. Despite the variety of techniques, these more-or-less official styles of painting may all be called Yamato-e (literally, Japanese painting), for they depicted strictly native Japanese themes, and often with emotional nuances not found in the arts of any other land.

Other variant styles of Yamato-e exist, and it is interesting to speculate on the number of painting workshops apart from the E-dokoro which may have been active in the Heian capital during the eleventh and twelfth centuries. Ateliers in some of the large Buddhist temples (Daigo-ji and Enryaku-ji, for example, or Tōji and Kōzan-ji) made cult images in large numbers in the traditional Buddhist manner; but their illustrated versions of the lives of saints and the histories of temples were influenced by the court styles. Within the city itself, there must also have been private studios capable of producing the rather simple and intimate pictures found on the Shitennō-ji fans—birds and flowers, genre scenes of babies bathing or women coming from the market, and episodes from popular novels. These various artists' groups must also have been in close contact, for during the twelfth century their styles became increasingly mixed.

The painting workshops turned to specialized craftsmen for their paper, brushes, and pigments, their gold and silver leaf; there were mounters of paintings and screens, fan-makers, and book-binders. Associated with them were cloth dyers, weavers, brocade makers, armorers, bronze casters, wood-workers, and masters of shell inlay and lacquer. The Heian capital must have been a giant reservoir of craftsmen whose taste and discernment grew in sophistication over the decades.

The power of these artistic traditions was borne out by their survival despite the political upheavals which began to rock the capital toward the end of the eleventh century. In 1086 the Emperor Shira-kawa, who had long hoped to restore real power to the Imperial family, followed an ancient Bud-dhist tradition by abdicating the throne and enter-ing a monastery. The main purpose of this custom had been to demonstrate that the path of a Buddhist monk was superior to that of a king, but Shirakawa used it to free himself from the ceremonial restric-tions of the semi-divine Japanese kingship. He and his successors exerted great political authority from their monastic retreats, while the Imperial Throne usually was occupied by a powerless child. During the rule of these Cloistered Emperors, however, the military clans who had long served the Fuji-waras in controlling the outlying provinces also began to seek greater authority for themselves. Between 1150 and 1185, one of these clans, the Taira family, succeeded in dominating the govern-ment. Although the Tairas occupied great man-sions in the capital their main base of power was in

Western Japan, and Miyajima, their family shrine in Hiroshima Bay, was as ornate and as richly endowed as any temple of the Fujiwaras.

The power of the Tairas was constantly challenged by another military clan, the Minamotos, and the years until 1185 were marked by intrigues, violent warfare, and great suffering among the commoners, both in the capital and in the countryside. In addition, a sequence of natural calamities heightened the mood of *Götterdämmerung* in the capital. Earthquakes struck in 1158 and again in 1185, when the ground trembled for nearly two months after the main shock. A terrible fire swept the city in 1177; in 1180 a famine occurred, followed by plague and a typhoon. Indeed, these tragic decades may have seemed the fulfillment of predictions about the Latter Days of the Law.

Despite these catastrophes the production of works of art, both Buddhist and secular, continued with remarkable vigor, their qualities of beauty and grace being cherished all the more. And yet by the early years of the thirteenth century distinct changes had appeared, even in those works which seem closest in form to their counterparts of the preceding century—Buddhist paintings, mirrors, and narrative scrolls. A more didactic and muscular spirit made itself felt, reflecting the changing conditions of national life under the rule of the Kamakura military government. Gone were a certain gentleness and deftness of line, a softness of coloring, a unity of design which had kept ornament from becoming obtrusive. In those subtle, almost intangible qualities, which disappeared as the Kamakura period ensued, we may recognize the last of the many gifts to the human spirit from the arts of Heian Japan.

Plates

ESOTERIC BUDDHIST ARTS

1a. OPPOSITE: *Portrait of Ryūjū Bosatsu (Nāgārjuna). Late 11th c. Color on silk;* H. *50¾ inches. (Shown only at Asia House Gallery.)*

2. *Gōzanze Myō-ō. 11th c. Wood;* H. 32¼ *inches.*

3. *Tobatsu Bishamon-ten. 10th–11th c. Wood with traces of gesso and color;* H. *49¼ inches.*

4. *Head of Aizen Myō–ō. First half of the 12th c. Joined wood;* H. 13½ *inches.*

5a. Page from a Notebook Depicting the Kongōkai Mandala; Kongōbu Bosatsu. Attributed to Takuma Tametō (active mid-12th c.). Ink and color on paper; H. *(originally) 9¹⁵⁄₁₆ inches.*

46

密号普救金剛

除蓋障并

種子 भ

三昧耶形

5c. Page from a Notebook Depicting the Kongōkai Mandala; Jōkaisho Bosatsu.

東
南
雲
金
剛
意
生
金
剛

種子

黒色

5d. Page from a Notebook Depicting the Kongōkai Mandala; Tōnanun Kongō.

6. *Wooden Cylinder for Tantric Ritual. Ca. 1150–1175. Sendan cedar with ink drawings;* H. *9¼ inches.*

7. *Ishana-ten. 12th c. Ink on paper;* H. *34¼ inches.*

8. *Fugen Enmei and the Four Guardian Kings. Mid–12th c. Color and cut gold on silk;* H. 55¹³⁄₁₆ *inches. (Shown only at the Fogg Art Museum.)*

9. *Dainichi as Ichijikinrin Seated on a Lotus Throne. Late 12th c. Color on silk;* H. *49⁵⁄₁₆ inches. (Shown only at the Fogg Art Museum.)*

9. Detail.

CLASSICAL BUDDHIST ARTS

10. *Seated Amida. Late 8th–9th c. Wood-core dry lacquer; H. 11⅝ inches.*

12. *Seated Buddha. Late 10th–early 11th c. Wood with traces of red paint;* H. 10¾ *inches.*

13. Jizō Bodhisattva. Ca. 900. Wood; H. 42 inches.

14. *Flying Angel. 10th c. Wood;* H. *18 inches.*

16. *Zōchō-ten, Guardian of the South. Mid-9th c. Wood with traces of gesso and color;* H. *52¾ inches. (Shown only at the Fogg Art Museum.)*

17. *Guardian General. Ca. early 10th c. Wood with thin lacquer coat and gold leaf;* H. *(figure)* 13¼ *inches.*

18. *Standing Guardian. Late 9th or early 10th c. Wood;* H. *(figure) 37 inches. (Shown only at Asia House Gallery.)*

19. Bishamon-ten, Guardian of the North. Ca. 1162. Woodblock print on paper; H. *(figure)* 6¹⁵⁄₁₆ *inches.*

20. *Head of Guardian. Last half of the 11th c. Assembled wood construction;* H. *12½ inches.*

21. Standing Bodhisattva. First half of the 11th c. Cypress wood with traces of paint; H. *(figure)* 35¹³⁄₁₆ *inches.*

22. Head of the Buddha. Mid-12th c. Assembled wood-block construction; H. 14⅛ *inches.*

23. Head and Torso of Bodhisattva. Mid-12th c. Assembled wood-block construction; H. 20¹³⁄₁₆ *inches.*

24. *Seated Yakushi. Second half of the 12th c. Cast bronze;* H. *10¾ inches.*

25. *Goddess Benzai-ten Playing a Lute. Late 12th c. Color on silk;* H. 47½ *inches.*

ARTS OF THE PURE LAND CREED

27. *Seated Amida Buddha. Late 11th–early 12th c. Polychromed wood; H. 32 inches.*

30. Standing Images of Shō Kannon. 12th c. Wood with traces of color; H. *(approx.) figures 15¼ inches, pedestals 3¾ inches.*
ABOVE: *c.* OPPOSITE: *a.and b.*

30. *Standing Images of Shō Kannon. 12th c. Wood with traces of color;* H. *(approx.) figures* 15¼ *inches, pedestals* 3¾ *inches.*
ABOVE: *f. (Shown only at the Fogg Art Museum.)* OPPOSITE: *e. (left) and d. (right).*

26. Cinerary Urn with Paradise Scenes. Early Heian period. Gilt bronze; H. 9¾ *inches.*

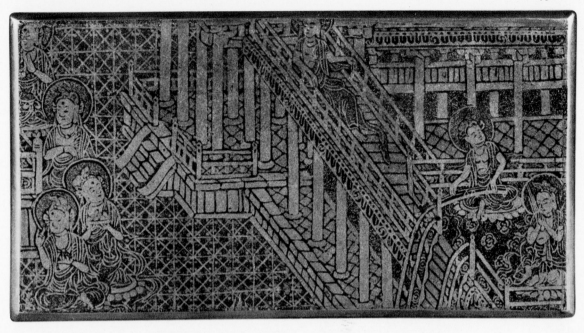

28. *Fragment of Scene of Amida's Paradise. Late Heian period. Lacquer on wood;* H. 3 1/16 *inches.*

74

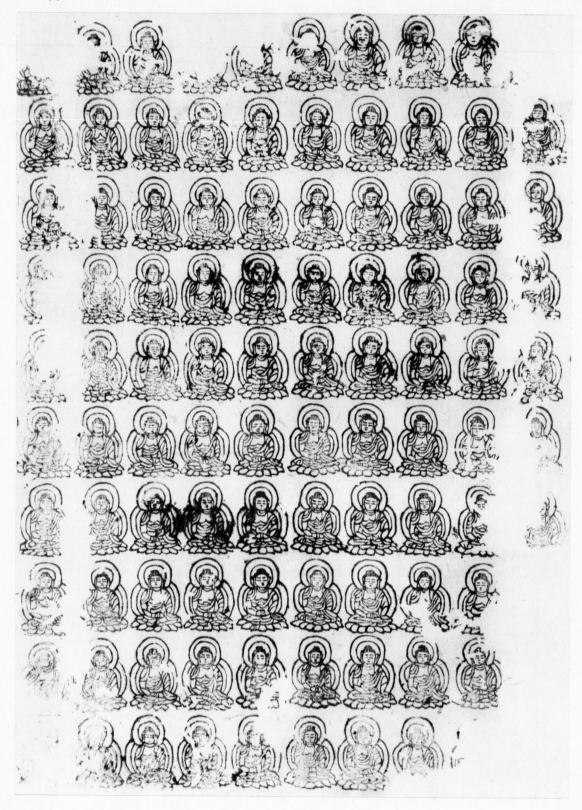

29. One Hundred Images of Amida Nyorai. Early 12th c. Woodblock print on paper; H. 17⅜ *inches.*

MASKS

31a. Processional Mask. One of the Jūni-ten. Late 10th–early 11th c. Wood with traces of lacquer and color; H. 11 inches.

32. Processional Mask. Late 10th–early 11th c. Wood with traces of lacquer; H. 9¼ inches.

33. Processional Mask. Mid–12th c. Wood, lacquered and painted; H. 8⅝ *inches.*

31b. Processional Mask. Bodhisattva. Late 10th–early 11th c. Wood with traces of lacquer and color; H. 8¼ *inches.*

ILLUMINATED SUTRAS

35. Frontispiece of Illuminated Sutra. Mid-12th c. Gold and silver ink on indigo paper; H. 10¾ *inches.*

34a. Illuminated Sutra from Chūson-ji. Daihanyaharamita-kyō (Māhaprajñāpāramitā-sūtra), Vol. 338. Mid-12th c. Gold and silver ink on indigo paper; H. *(frontispiece)* 10 1/16 *inches.*

34b. Illuminated Sutra from Chūson-ji. Daihanyaharamita-kyō, Vol. 582. Mid-12th c. Gold and silver ink on indigo paper; H. *(frontispiece)* 10 1/16 *inches.*

36. Illuminated Sutra from Jingo-ji. Last half 12th c. Gold and silver ink on blue paper; H. (frontispiece) 10¹⁄₁₆ inches

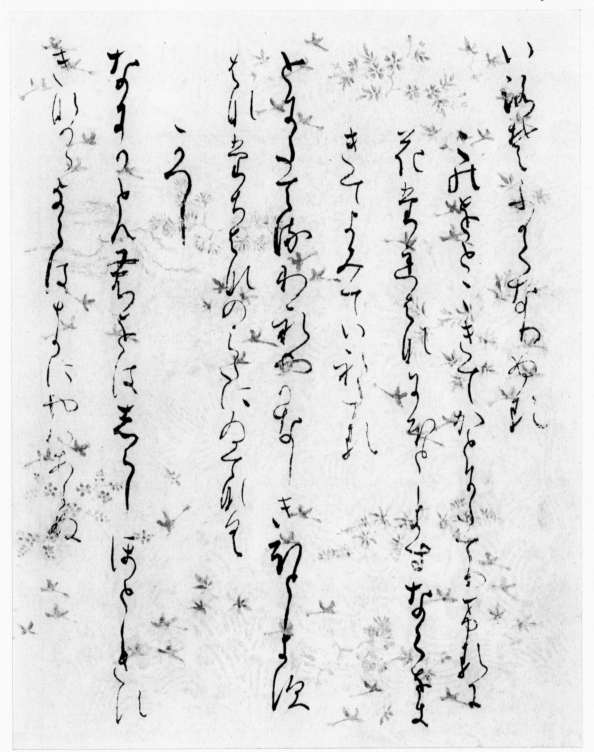

CALLIGRAPHY AND ILLUSTRATION

37d. Single page from the Collected Poems of Ise (Ise-shū). Early 12th c. Ink on ornamented paper; H. *7¹⁵⁄₁₆ inches (approx.).*

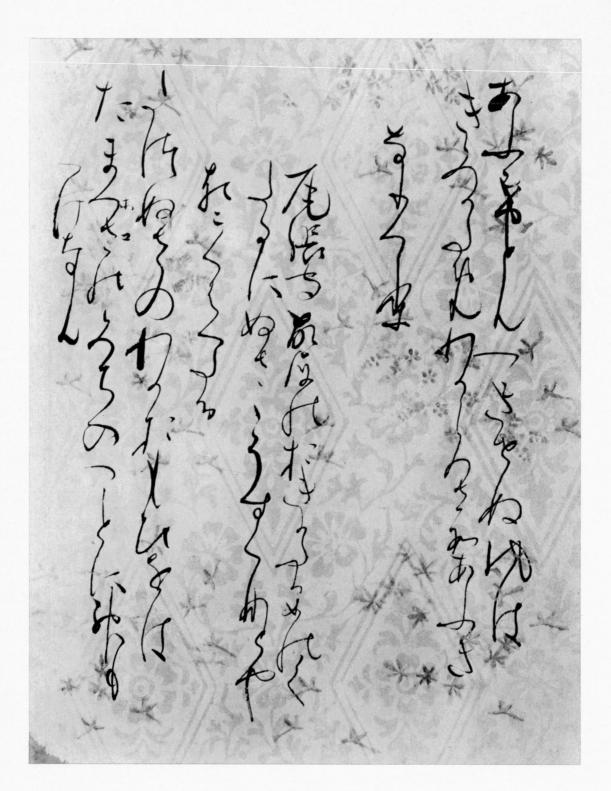

37b. Single page from the Collected Poems of Tsurayuki. Early 12th c. Ink on ornamented paper; H. 7¹⁵⁄₁₆ *inches (approx.).*

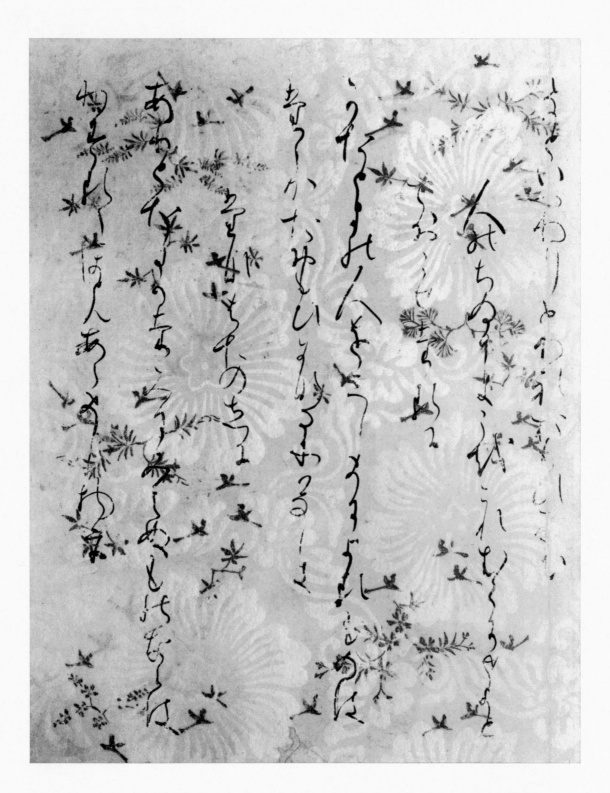

37c. Single page from the Collected Poems of Ise (Ise-shū). Early 12th c. Ink on ornamented paper; н. 7¹⁵⁄₁₆ inches (approx.).

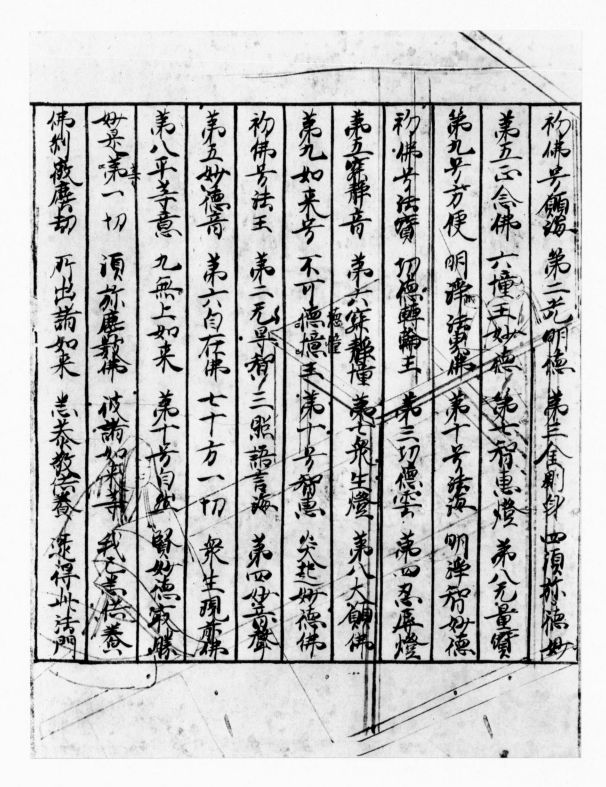

38. Section from the "Menashi-gyō." Ca. 1160–1170 (text inscribed in 1193). Ink on paper, guide lines in silver; H. 10¾ inches.

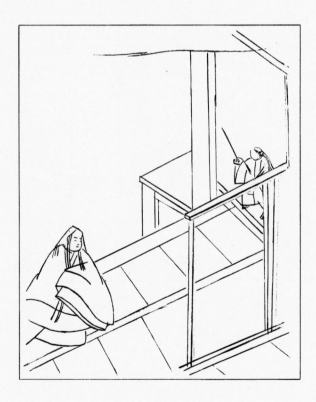

38. Underdrawing of Section from the "Menashi-gyō."

88

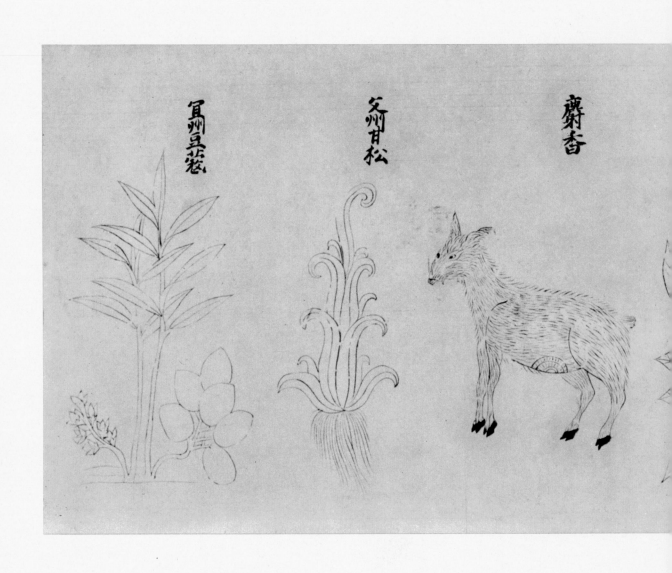

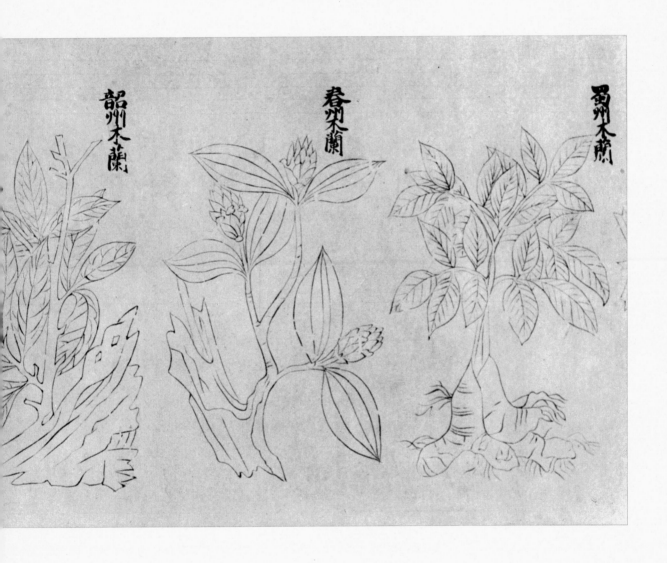

40. *Treatise on Medicines and Incense by Shōken. Mid-12th c. Handscroll, ink on paper;* H. 11 *inches.*

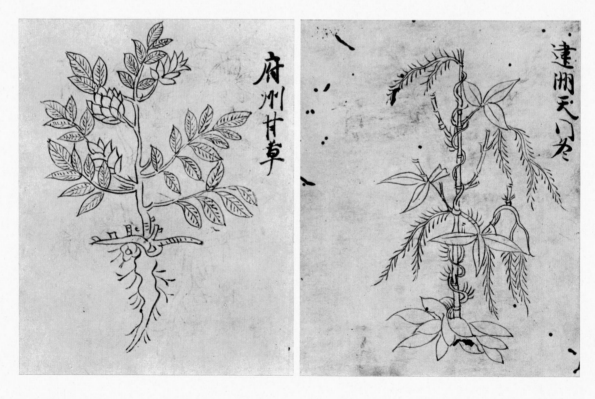

府州甘草　　達州天门冬

39a. and b. Pages from a Yakushu-shō (Materia Medica) *by Keni Ajari. Late 12th c. Book form;* H. 6⅝ *inches.*

42. *Head of Monk's Staff. Late 12th c. Cast bronze; H. 9¼ inches.*

92

41. Alms Bowl. 10th c. Gilt bronze; ʜ. *5 inches.*

43. Mirror with Design of Two Birds and Flowers. 12th c. Bronze; diam. 5¼ inches.

44. *Mirror with Design of Cranes and Pine Needles. Ca. 11th–12th c. Cast bronze; diam. 4⅛ inches.*

45. LOWER LEFT: *Mirror with Design of Sparrows and Chrysanthemums. Ca. 11th–12th c. Cast bronze; diam. 3⅝ inches.*
46. UPPER RIGHT: *Mirror with Design of Cranes and Pine Needles. 11th–12th c. Cast bronze; diam. 3³⁄₁₆ inches.*

47. *Mirror with Design of Reeds or Grass. Late Heian period. Cast bronze; diam. 3½ inches.*

48. *Mirror with Engraved Design of Zaō Gongen. 11th–12th c. Copper alloy; diam. 9¹¹⁄₁₆ inches.*

49. *Zaō Gongen. 11th–12th c. Bronze plaque;* H. 15½ *inches.*

50. *Zaō Gongen. 11th c. Bronze plaque; H. 8¼ inches.*

51. *Zaō Gongen. 12th c. Hollow-cast bronze;* H. 10⅜ *inches.*

CERAMICS

52. *Sue Ware Bottle. 9th–10th c. Grey pottery with ash glaze;* H. *8 inches.*

54. Sue Ware Jar. 9th–10th c. Pottery with ash glaze; H. 8¹⁵⁄₁₆ *inches.*

53. Covered Jar. 9th c. Grey pottery with ash glaze; H. 8¼ *inches.*

56. *Roof Tile. Early Heian period. Grey clay; diam. 7¼ inches.*   55. *Roof Tile. Late 8th c. Grey clay; diam. 7¼ inches.*

57. *Roof Tile. Late 12th c. Grey clay; diam. 11 inches.*

Catalogue

ABBREVIATIONS

Kimpuzen   *Kimpuzen Kyōzuka Ibutsu no Kenkyū (Relics of the Kimpuzen Sūtra Mound)*, Imperial Museum Reports, No. 8. Tokyo, 1937.
Kokuhō   *Kokuhō. The National Treasures of Japan*. Vol. I, up to the eighth century; Vol. II, early Heian period; Vol. III, late Heian period; Vol. IV, early Kamakura period; Vol. V, later Kamakura period. Tokyo, 1964–1966.
Kuno   Kuno, Takeshi. *A Guide to Japanese Sculpture*. Tokyo, 1963.
Lee   Lee, Sherman E. *Japanese Decorative Style*. Cleveland, 1961.
Mayuyama   Mayuyama, Junkichi. *Japanese Art in the West*. Tokyo, 1966.
SBZS   *Sekai Bijutsu Zenshū*. Vol. III, Nara period; Vol. IV, early Heian period; Vol. V, late Heian period; Vol. VI, Kamakura period. Tokyo: Kadokawa Shoten, 1961–1962.

CATALOGUE

1 PAINTINGS FROM A SET OF PORTRAITS OF SHŌTOKU TASHI AND THE PATRIARCHS OF THE TENDAI SECT
Late eleventh century
Color on silk; H. 50¾ in. (128.8 cm.), W. 29⅞ in. (75.8 cm.)
Ichijō-ji, Hyogo prefecture
Registered National Treasures

The major Buddhist sects of China and Japan gave great prominence to paintings and statues of their patriarchs, in order to demonstrate the channels through which their doctrines had been transmitted over the centuries—from India to the lands of the East. Placed in pagodas and temple halls and made the objects of commemorative services, these images were regarded as certificates of the orthodoxy of the faith.

Ten paintings from Ichijō-ji are the oldest remaining portraits of the patriarchs of the Tendai sect. Inscriptions on five of them suggest that their texts (if not the pictures themselves) were copied from originals which were in existence in A.D. 946 on the walls of a building at the Tendai headquarters of Enryaku-ji temple, atop Mt. Hiei. Although the prototypes have disappeared, we may imagine that these Tendai portraits originated in much the same manner as the patriarchal images of the Shingon sect, which are better documented. Of these, the monk Kūkai brought back from China in the year 806 five remarkably realistic portraits done by the artist Li-chen of Ch'ang-an. Three others were eventually added, and the Shingon set of eight portraits (still in existence at Tōji in Kyoto although in ruinous condition now) was copied countless times. Copies

were installed in all of the Shingon temples (*Kokuhō*, Vol. II, Pls. 62, 63).

The two late eleventh century portraits shown here are from the set painted for Ichijō-ji, an important Tendai monastery secluded in the hills north of Himeji. Stylistically they combine, with remarkable skill, two rather different artistic approaches. The spirit of descriptive portraiture is present, a legacy of the T'ang Chinese origins of this traditional series; on the other hand, there is a strong decorative quality, the native Japanese instinct for design, which became increasingly evident in late Heian times. Clues to the date of the paintings—similarities in the treatment of garment folds, facial expressions, and surface decoration—may be seen in the "Nirvāna of the Buddha" at Kōyasan, painted in 1086, and the large "Shaka Emerging from his Golden Coffin" dating from the late eleventh century, formerly in Chōhō-ji (*Kokuhō*, Vol. II, Pls. 6–10).

The Ichijō-ji paintings have been considerably restored and repainted over the centuries, and their borders have been cut down. The identity of some of the patriarchs is not entirely certain, for some of the colophons have been lost. Nevertheless the portraits are among those rare works in which both artistic and historical content are of the highest level of importance.

a. PORTRAIT OF RYŪJŪ BOSATSU (NĀGĀRJUNA)
In this idealized portrait a monk is placed upon an ornate lotus throne and given a halo as though he were a divinity; he holds both a teaching baton (*nyo-i*) and an incense burner. The most likely identification is Nāgārjuna, an Indian theologian of the second or third century A.D.,

revered in China and Japan as a Bodhisattva incarnate in the first mortal teacher of Esoteric Buddhist doctrines. According to the traditions of the Ichijō-ji monastery this is the portrait of Asvaghosha (Memyō Bosatsu), the brilliant Indian theologian, poet, and playwright of the second century A.D. Modern scholarship, however, has tended to identify it as Nāgārjuna, whose likeness is also first in the set of portraits of Shingon patriarchs at Tōji. The figure is imbued with a remarkable sense of dignity and composure, while the lyrical interplay of the patterns of garment folds and their surface ornamentation reflect the florid decorative sense of the later Heian period. *Illus. p. 40.*

b. PORTRAIT OF SHŌTOKU TAISHI

Shōtoku Taishi (572–621) was revered in Japan as the man who successfully established the Buddhist faith at the apex of Japanese cultural and religious life. No realistic images of the Prince date from his lifetime; this hieratic portrait shows him in an idealized guise, as a youth seated upon a low dais and holding a long-handled incense burner. Before him ten children kneel in gestures of adoration. They are his childhood playmates, but he towers over them in exaggerated, hieratic scale.

Prince Shōtoku's presence in this set of patriarchal portraits may be explained by the legend that he was the reincarnation of the Chinese Tendai master Hui-ssu (515–577), who died about the time of Shōtoku's birth. This legend was commonly recognized in China as well as in Japan (see E. Reischauer, *Ennin's Diary* [New York, 1955], pp. 36, 57, 78n). Hui-ssu was the teacher of the greatest of the Chinese Tendai sages, Chih-i (or T'ien-tai Ta-shih), and both men are presumably represented in the Ichijō-ji set of portraits. *Illus. frontispiece.*

Published: *Kokuhō*, Vol. II, Pls. 85, 86; *Kokka*, No. 275 (1913), p. 241 ff; *Bijutsu Kenkyū*, 53 (May, 1936), p. 206. *Shown only at Asia House Gallery*

2 GŌZANZE MYŌ-Ō
Eleventh century
Wood; H. 32¼ in. (81.9 cm.)
Los Angeles County Museum of Art

In Esoteric Buddhist art, the Bright Kings (Myō-ō) symbolise the awesome power brought to bear against heresy and spiritual obstacles. Gōzanze is the wrathful incarnation

of the Buddha Akshobhya; his original name in Sanskrit is Trailokyavijaya, or Conqueror of the Three Realms—desire, resentment, and stupidity.

This figure is carved essentially out of a single block of wood, and in the back is a shallow, square recess with a deep, round hole penetrating the body, probably for the insertion of dedicatory objects (see Nos. 19 and 29). The deity has four faces, one of them turned to the rear; originally he had eight arms, and trampled beneath his striding feet two demonic forms symbolic of Siva and his consort Uma. The suggested triumph over the heresy of Hinduism is borne out by the other Saivite elements in the make-up of Gōzanze: the name Trailokyavijaya itself is that of Siva, and so also are the weapons Gōzanze usually brandishes—the trident, noose, thunderbolt, and bow and arrow.

This work is imbued with a strong degree of violent energy, but its force does not equal that of the earliest Myō-ō statues in Japan, those of the 830's in the Tōji Lecture Hall, which are thicker and carved in deeper relief. In its more slender proportions, shallow surface carving, and linear drapery, the Los Angeles figure may be compared with carvings from Daigo-ji, such as the Nyoirin Kannon of the late eleventh century, or the Emma-ō of Upper Daigo of the early twelfth century. *Illus. p. 42.*

Published: Mayuyama, No. 37.

3 TOBATSU BISHAMON-TEN
Tenth-eleventh century
Wood with traces of gesso and color; H. 49¼ in. (125 cm.)
Howard C. Hollis, New York

Tobatsu Bishamon-ten is a special manifestation of the Guardian King of the North, Vaiśravana (Bishamon-ten or Tamon-ten in Japanese). The origin of this deity may be traced to Central Asia, where it was worshipped independently and particularly revered as a protector of cities. The Tōji temple in Kyoto has a famous wooden statue of this god, brought from China early in the Heian period and said to have been installed originally in the main gate of the capital (the Rashōmon) in order to guarantee the city's safety and well-being (*Kokuhō*, Vol. II, Pls. 55, 56).

The exotic appearance of Tobatsu Bishamon-ten, with his long tunic, armor, and high crown, attests to his Central Asian origin. This is also apparent in the bust of the Earth Goddess Prthivi (Jiten in Japanese) who supports the deity, an essential part of these figures from their inception. From about the tenth century on, gradual modifications appeared in Japanese versions of this type of image and certain Central Asiatic features, such as the armored skirt, began to disappear. The Hollis piece belongs to this phase. Although it is still basically similar to the ninth century prototypes, accommodations to native taste may be seen in the Earth Goddess, who has strong similarities to Shinto figures, and in the carving of the body from a single block of wood. A unique feature of this statue is the representation of five small seated Buddhas, now quite worn, on the front of the crown. The left arm is not original.

The Tobatsu Bishamon-ten is not, strictly speaking, an Esoteric Buddhist deity. He is not portrayed in the mandalas, but the introduction and flourishing of his cult in Japan coincided with the coming of Mikkyō, and it was often practiced in Mikkyō temples. *Illus. p. 43.*

Published: Mayuyama, No. 18; Kazuko Ikawa, "Statues of Bishamon-ten Supported by Chiten; Research on the So-called Tobatsu Bishamon," *Bijutsu Kenkyū* (July, 1963), No. 229.

4   HEAD OF AIZEN MYŌ-Ō
     First half of the twelfth century
     Joined wood; H. 13½ in. (34.3 cm.)
     John G. Powers, New York

Many seated figures of Aizen are found which date from the Kamakura period and later. Usually they are painted a deep red, crowned with a scowling lion, given six arms, and placed before a red-black circular halo—a most frightening, awesome icon. Very few sculptural examples have been preserved from the Heian period and this head may be among the oldest. Characteristic of a date in the first half of the twelfth century are the broad head in which the eyes and nose are closely joined, the strong sense of volumetric unity about the head as a whole, and a rather genial expression. Also typical of this date is the method of hollow wood construction—two thin, rounded, shells of wood joined vertically behind the ears.

Aizen is not included in the group of the Five Great Myō-ō so often featured in major Mikkyō sculpture projects. Instead he often serves as an independent object of worship within his own shrine. He symbolizes one of the most fundamental Mahāyāna Buddhist conceptions, namely that illusion and human passions are identical with enlightenment, that the metaphysical ground of all being permeates even that which can be called illusory and morally evil. Man in an enlightened state of insight, filled with the rapture of pure wisdom, loses all sense of discrimination between good and evil, ugliness and beauty— for these are relative conceptions, the products of our own interpretation of things, hence essentially unreal. Only the dharma of the Buddha is real and enduring. *Illus. p. 44.*

5   PAGES FROM A NOTEBOOK DEPICTING THE KONGŌ-
     KAI MANDALA
     Attributed to Takuma Tametō (active mid-twelfth century)
     Ink and color on paper; each originally H. 9¹⁵⁄₁₆ in. (25.3 cm.), W. 5⁹⁄₁₆ in. (14.2 cm.)
     a. Mr. and Mrs. Solomon Diamond, Pasadena
     b. Anonymous loan
     c. University of Michigan Museum of Art, Ann Arbor
     d. John G. Powers, New York

An ancient illustrated handbook for Shingon monks was discovered in 1936 in Ganjō-ji, a small temple in Kyūshū, in Kuma county, Kumamoto prefecture, by a group of specialists from the Japanese Commission for the Protection of Cultural Properties. The book was sold before legal steps to register and protect it could be completed and the individual leaves were cut apart and distributed among collectors in Japan and abroad. Twelve pages are now in the Museum of the Yamato Bunkakan in Nara (*Selected Catalogue of the Museum* [Nara, 1960], No. 5), and five in the Mutō collection, Kobe.

The pages in the Mutō collection are simple black and white drawings of mandalas in large, double-page format; the remainder of the book consists of 95 pages, each showing, in delicately tinted colors, one deity of the Kongōkai Mandala. Each sheet ordinarily bears the name of the deity in both Chinese and Sanskrit characters, then its "secret names," a description of its coloring, its Shūji or

Sanskrit "seed" initial, and an illustration of the symbolic device which represents the deity on an altar.

Judging from the inscriptions on the final page, the book was treasured for centuries by monks of the Shingon sect. The earliest, dated in 1420, states that the book had been kept on Mount Kōya (mountain headquarters of the Shingon sect), in the northern hostel of the Kōdai-in, and that it had been given by a certain monk Chōson to one named Kōshin. An inscription dated 1532 records its presentation to the Abbot of the Ganjō-ji, where it was discovered. Another sheet, bearing the same date, attributes the book to "the painter Shōchi, whose popular name was Takuma Tametō of Bungo, whose ecclesiastical rank was Hōin (Seal of the Law)."

Tametō was a member of the Takuma family, Buddhist monk-painters active for over five hundred years and important figures in pre-modern Japanese accounts of the history of painting. One distinguished member, Tamenari, was said to have done the wall paintings of the Phoenix Hall of the Byōdō-in at Uji. The attribution of this notebook to the hand of Tametō is not certain, but Tanaka has pointed out several factors which tend more to confirm than deny it. In any event, the drawings are superlative examples of Buddhist painting which would be placed in the mid-twelfth century on stylistic grounds alone. They display an exceedingly professional level of execution and control.

In one of its inscriptions, the notebook is given the name *Kontai Butsuga-chō* (Notebook of the Buddhist paintings of the Golden Body), but this seems to be an abbreviated reference to the two standard mandalas of the Shingon sect, the Kongōkai and the Taizōkai. Hence the book may well have been one of a pair which depicted both mandalas.

a. KONGŌBU BOSATSU

This sheet was probably No. 29 of the colored drawings in the original book. The inscriptions are as follows: *upper right*, Kongōbu Bosatsu; *upper left*, "Secret Name" Myōtō Kongō (Vajra of the miraculous path) and also Shinto Kongō (Vajra of the divine path); *lower right* gives the Sanskrit Vajra Nritiya and the sound transcribed into Chinese characters, and also designates the coloring as light blue, and stipulates that the deity's symbol (Sammaiya-gyō) is the Katsuma-shō, a four-fold thunderbolt which is shown below; *lower left*, the Sanskrit Shūji *krit. Illus. p. 45.*

b. KONGŌKE BOSATSU

This sheet was No. 31 in the original book. The inscriptions are as follows: *upper right*, Kongōke Bosatsu (Vajra-flower Bodhisattva); *upper left*, "Secret Name" Myōshiki Kongō (Vajra of miraculous color) and also Shōjō Kongō (Vajra of purity); *lower right* gives the Sanskrit Vajra Pushpā (Thunderbolt flower) and the sounds transcribed into Chinese characters as Bazara Pushupa, designates the coloring as light yellow, and suggests that the flowers shown below are its symbol; *lower left*, the Sanskrit Shūji *Om. Illus. p. 14.*

c. JOKAISHŌ BOSATSU

This was No. 40 of the original set. The inscriptions are as follows: *upper right*, Jokaishō Bosatsu (the Bodhisattva who dispels spiritual hindrances); *upper left*, "Secret Name" Jugen Kongō (the all-powerful Vajra); *lower right*, Sammaiya-gyō (a reference to the treasure box, placed before him on a lotus, as the deity's emblem); *lower left*, Shūji (?) *Yam. Illus. p. 46.*

d. TŌNANUN KONGŌ

This was No. 79 of the original set of colored drawings. The inscriptions are as follows: *upper right*, Tōnanun Kongō (Vajra of the southeastern cloud) and also Ishō Kongō (Vajra produced by the will); *lower left*, the Chinese character Shūji, but without the Sanskrit letter, and the stipulation that the color is black. *Illus. p. 47.*

Published: Ichimatsu Tanaka, "Kontai Butsuga-chō to Takuma Tametō," *Yamato Bunka*, XII (December, 1963), pp. 28–37; the same author's *Nihon Kaigashiron-shū*, Tokyo, 1965, pp. 100–121.

6 WOODEN CYLINDER FOR TANTRIC RITUAL

Ca. 1150–1175
Sendan cedar with ink drawings; H. 9¼ in. (23.5 cm.) including lids, DIAM. 2 1/16 in. (5.28 cm.)
John G. Powers, New York

This small wooden cylinder, painted with the images of protective deities, served in an Esoteric Buddhist ritual called the Tembōrin-hō, "Turning the Wheel of the Law." The patron of this ceremony inscribed on a piece of paper the desired goals—safe childbirth, tranquility for a city or nation, victory over enemies—and inserted it into the cylinder. A group of monks then placed the cylinder before the image of an appropriate deity such as Jizō or Fudō, Maitreya, or the Ichijikinrin Dainichi; with chanting of the appropriate texts, incense was burned and a Goma fire built. When the goal was the dispelling of an evil state of the spirit, or when the suppliant wished harm to an enemy, the inserted paper would be removed and burned.

The ritual was first introduced to Japan from T'ang China in the ninth century by the monks Kūkai and Ennin, but it did not become prominent until the twelfth and thirteenth centuries; it was especially practised by Shingon monks. For example, following the great fire of 1177, which destroyed twenty thousand homes and killed a thousand people in the Heian Kyō, the Retired Emperor Goshirakawa ordered the ceremony performed for seven days in order to restore tranquility.

A square piece of paper found in this tube bears the seal of Kōzan-ji and writing appears on both sides. The obverse has a design of five concentric circles with Sanskrit characters representing various deities; on the reverse is a similar design together with the Sanskrit formula invoking the power of the deity Marici, who guarded against the perils of war. It gives the name of Fujiwara Yasuie, a courtier of the "junior fifth rank upper grade." In one corner is the notation that this design was copied at Kōyasan in 1205 from one used in a ceremony on August 11, 1175, to increase the good fortune of Yasuie (who died in 1210).

On the body of the cylinder are delineated the images of sixteen gods of protection and good fortune, shown in four registers, with the name of each written in vertical Sanskrit letters. The two upper registers are filled with ten Yakshas from the Indian tradition of tutelary guardians of specific locales or kinds of fortune. The first is none other than Viśvakarma, the Indian father of the arts; also shown are Manibhadra, giver of wealth, and Virūpāksha, who is also Kōmokuten, one of the Four Deva Kings (Shitennō). On the next register are three Nagarajas, led by Vasuki, who is famous in Indian Epic mythology as the serpent used in the churning of the ocean; on the lower register are three Goddesses, led by Hāritī, goddess of fertility.

The top and bottom lids of the cylinder are carved in low relief in the shape of the *dharmacakra*, and on both sides of the cylinder Sanskrit letters are written in ink. The wood used is an aromatic form of cedar which is specif-

ically prescribed in the ancient liturgical manuals under its old name, *kuremboku*. The surface is glossy, partly because it was coated with a reddish translucent pigment which has since darkened.

The images were lightly scratched into the soft wood and then the drawing in *sumi* ink was rapidly and skillfully brushed in. In a meticulous article from which much of this information was drawn, Taka Yanagisawa has shown that the style employed belongs roughly to the third quarter of the twelfth century, and that the cylinder may well have been kept at the Kajū-ji (Kanshū-ji) monastery near Uji and then given to the famous monk Myōe Shōnin of Kōzan-ji in 1214. A cylinder similar to this one but brightly colored in the style of the mid-thirteenth century has been preserved at Kōzan-ji, and there is a bronze cylinder with the same designs at Ninna-ji. *Illus. p. 48.*

Published: Taka Yanagisawa, "Three Examples of the Tembōrin Cylinder with Painted or Incised Figures . . ." (in Japanese, with English summary), *Bijutsu Kenkyū* (November, 1963), No. 231, pp. 1–22.

7   ISHANA-TEN

Twelfth century

Ink on paper; H. 34¼ in. (86 cm.), W. 17⅞ in. (45.5 cm.)

Anonymous loan

This large drawing, made in a Buddhist painting workshop, was intended as a guide to artists for the preparation of a colored version, probably on silk. It carries color notes, and also shows the correction of the workshop master in the independent sketch of the right hand, which is far more articulate in line and structure than is the hand on the figure. In the upper right-hand corner, written beneath the name of the deity, is the name Chinkai, that of an important theologian, calligrapher, and painter. Born in Kyoto in 1092, he rose to the rank of Chief of Instruction at Daigo-ji and took a prominent part in some of the great public ceremonies of his day. He produced drawings and paintings, especially of mandalas, and he also repaired older works. Pictures attributed to him have been preserved at Kōzan-ji, Tōji, and Daigo-ji; especially famous is the painting "Monju Crossing the Sea" at the Kōdai-in. The name Daigo-ji appears in the upper left corner of this drawing, one of a set of twelve representations of Jūni-ten, along with Sambō-in, the Abbott's quarters, and the series name, Jūni-ten.

Ishana-ten was one of the twelve guardian devas whose images were displayed in Shingon ceremonies, especially the rite customarily performed in the Imperial Palace compound on January 8th, to invoke the well-being of the Emperor and nation. Among the twelve deities, all purely Indian in origin, were Indra, chief of the gods, Agni, god of fire, and the sun and moon gods Sūrya and Chandra. In Sanskrit, Iśāna is one of the epithets of Śiva, and the Buddhist explanations leave little doubt that the mighty god of the Hindu pantheon has here been given a Buddhist guise and reduced to the role of a guardian protector. In this drawing, Śiva's trident is held in the left hand, a cup of blood in the right. The face, with fangs and a third eye, has a fierce expression; three skulls adorn his necklace. But these frightful elements of Tantric Buddhism, which also appear prominently in Tibetan Lamaist art, are here strangely softened, as though the innate restraint and decorum of Japanese taste had purged their horrendous spirit. *Illus. p. 49.*

Published: *Kokuhō*, Vol. III, p. 5, Fig. 3.

This painting would have been hung as the main object of worship at an Enmei-hō, an Esoteric ceremony intended to bring prolonged life, prosperity, and wisdom to the devotee. On one occasion, in 1076, the rite was performed in a detached Imperial Palace by the Abbot of Hōshō-ji and twenty acolytes, and continued for five days; another ceremony held in 1081 lasted for seventeen days.

Despite the Tantric symbolism, there is in this painting much of the visionary and lyrical beauty of Buddhist art of the twelfth century, especially in the transparencies and rhythmical movements of the drapery and scarves. This work has much in common with the chief dated landmark of later Heian period painting, the large Jūni-ten of Tōji, dated 1127; but its line quality is somewhat harder and the composition tighter and more schematic. There are close similarities between this figure of Fugen and that of the celebrated Kujaku Myō-ō of this same period (*Kokuhō*, Vol. III, Pls. 13–15). *Illus. p. 50.*

Published: Mayuyama, No. 71; Masaharu Anesaki, *Buddhist Art in Relation to Buddhist Ideals*, Boston, 1915, Pl. XXVI.

Shown only at the Fogg Art Museum

8 FUGEN ENMEI AND THE FOUR GUARDIAN KINGS
Mid-twelfth century
Color and cut gold on silk; H. 55 13/16 in. (141.7 cm.), w. 34 1/16 in. (88.1 cm.)
Museum of Fine Arts, Boston; Fenollosa-Weld Collection

In many ways this image of the Esoteric form of the Bodhisattva Fugen is ruled by the super-rational energies and imagination of Tantric art. The deity, his body pallid white, sits in rigid frontality, his legs crossed. He holds in his right hand the three-pronged thunderbolt and in his left the bell with a thunderbolt handle. The Five Wisdom Buddhas are placed in his crown. His mount is a four-headed elephant three of whose heads are visible, each scowling and each bearing six tusks. This beast stands upon a giant *Kongōrin*, a Wheel of Law, which in turn rests upon the backs of eight small elephants. Flanking this group are the four angry Guardian Kings, their scarves and flaming halos blown by the wind; Bishamon stands at the upper left holding a stupa in his hand.

9 DAINICHI AS ICHIJIKINRIN SEATED ON A LOTUS THRONE
Late twelfth century
Color on silk; H. 49 7/16 in. (125.5 cm.), w. 31¼ in. (79.4 cm.)
Museum of Fine Arts, Boston; Ross Collection

In this form, Dainichi is symbolized as the embodiment of the wisdom of the Buddha concentrated in the *ushnisha*, or cranial lump; and the universality of his creed is denoted by the Golden Wheel of the Law, suspended around his neck.

Here Dainichi sits cross-legged on a white lotus, holding his hands in the Chiken-in gesture ("the Fist of Wisdom"), the right hand, symbolic of the noumenal realm of the spirit, enclosing the left which symbolizes phenomenal matter. In his headdress are the Five Wisdom Buddhas (Gochi Nyorai), and around it is the radiant, swirling pattern which suggests his role as the source of all being. This form is indeed very close to that given to Dainichi in the central sector of the Taizōkai mandala as the emblem of the process by which the innate, divine ground of existence is converted into matter.

This painting, although slightly rubbed and worn, is among the earliest and most eloquent of the many versions of this theme. Characteristic of a date in the late Heian period are the low value contrasts, the soft mother-of-pearl tonality in the light colors, the integration of the surface design of jewelry and brocade with the background, and the lightly brushed color of the flaming halo. It is close in style, if more delicate and detailed, to the painting of the Butsugen Butsumo at Kōzan-ji which is inscribed by the monk Myōe Shōnin and given a *terminus ante quem* date of 1195 (*SBZS*, Vol. VI, Color Pl. 3; *Kokuhō*, Vol. V, No. 35). *Illus. pp. 51, 52.*

Shown only at the Fogg Art Museum

10 SEATED AMIDA
Late eighth–early ninth century
Wood-core dry lacquer; H. 11⅝ in. (29.5 cm.)
John G. Powers, New York

In both style and material, this delicate figure belongs to the time of transition from Nara period to early Heian modes of sculpture. In its symmetry and idealization of form it retains the spirit of the classical style; in addition, a touch of Nara period realism may be detected in the handling of the folds of the garment as it falls over the left arm and right ankle. Freedom and élan in the composition link it with such late Nara works as the seated Buddhas of wood-core dry lacquer that were placed in the base of the pagoda of Saidai-ji (*SBZS*, Vol. III, Pl. 26), or such early Heian works as the Buddha of Jingo-ji, done in the same medium (*SBZS*, Vol. IV, Fig. 27).

Seated cross-legged, the Buddha holds his hands in the gesture called *gebon chushō*, the emblem of his welcoming to Paradise even those who have sinned and broken the Buddhist commandments. (The fourth finger of the left hand, now missing, originally touched the thumb.) Amida images are found with nine such hand gestures, each symbolic of one of the nine stages of Paradise which are assigned to the nine levels of virtue (or lack of it) among men, ranging from saintly purity to gross evil. Some of the hair curls have been lost; they were made of separate pieces of wood and lacquer and attached to the surface. Elsewhere,

a coating of dry lacquer was thickly applied to the underlying wood blocks, and all the surface details subtly modeled in this pliable medium. *Illus. p. 53.*

Published: Mayuyama, No. 6.

11 THE BODHISATTVA NIKKŌ
Early ninth century
Japanese yew wood; H. 18⅜ inches (46.7 cm.)
The Cleveland Museum of Art

Carved with flawless skill and beautifully preserved, this small image of Nikkō is one of two Bodhisattvas which once flanked a statue of the Healing Buddha Yakushi Nyorai. The two attendants, representing the Luster of the Sun and Moon, did not in themselves express strong religious values but they enhanced those of Yakushi, one of the most widely worshipped deities in early Japanese Buddhism.

The sculptor of this figure was strongly motivated by the spirit of the Classical Buddhist style. He imbued the face with a sense of timeless composure; its heavy lips, strong nose, and smooth contours were derived ultimately from Indian canons of form of the Gupta period. The body does not sit erectly upright, but is bent in a lateral, curving axis, the left shoulder falling slightly lower than the right, the head canted to the left. The drapery hangs in relaxed, graceful movements, but the folds, even though carved in shallow relief, have the sharp ridges of the *hompa-shiki* (rolling-wave) style characteristic of early Heian sculpture. These ridges cast distinct, sharp shadows and strengthen the play of light and dark over the surface.

Near the pearl diadem are holes which suggest that a crown of wood or copper had once been added. The *urna* is made of carved crystal inserted between the eyes. Traces of polychromy are found about the hair, the jewelry, and the solar disc at the base of the top knot, but the main part of the figure was unpainted. It was thus one of a class of figures called *danzō*, made of rare, imported sandal wood or any other aromatic or especially close-grained woods valued as fine materials in their own right. Stylistically, it has many points in common with *danzō* of the early Heian period done in the Classic Buddhist style: the Eleven-headed Kannon of Kōgen-ji (Fig. 3, p. 24), for example, or the same deity at Dōmyō-ji in Osaka prefecture (*Nihon Bunkashi Taikei*, Vol. IV, Tokyo, 1958, Fig. 360). *Illus. p. 8.*

Published: *Bulletin of The Cleveland Museum of Art*, LXVIII
(December, 1961), pp. 259–265; Mayuyama, No. 17.
Shown only at Asia House Gallery

12 SEATED BUDDHA
Late tenth–early eleventh century
Wood with traces of red paint; H. 10¾ in. (27.3 cm.)
John G. Powers, New York

Legacies from the sober style of solid wood sculpture
which began in Nara in the late eighth century—a sense
of mass and an air of settled composure and inherent
dignity—are seen in this seated Buddha carved from a
single block of wood. Its position relatively late in this
tradition, however, is shown by the flattened folds of the
robe, which are arranged across the chest in geometrically
precise curves, and by the hair curls, which have been
carved from the original block of wood rather than added
separately. The right hand, which extends forward in the
gesture of donation, appears to have been slightly recut.

The treatment of drapery is very close to that of the
seated Yakushi of 1013 at Kōfuku-ji; the low silhouette of
the body and the heavy jowls resemble those of the Yakushi
of Zensui-ji, Shiga prefecture, of 992 (Kuno, Pls. 64, 66).
Illus. p. 54.

13 JIZŌ BODHISATTVA
Ca. 900
Wood; H. 42 in. (109.8 cm.)
The Art Museum, Princeton University

The Bodhisattva Jizō, whose cult was introduced to Japan
in the mid-eighth century, was widely worshipped as a
deity deeply concerned with the needs of humble and
suffering humanity—women in childbirth, small children,
warriors on the battlefield, and the souls of the wicked or
misguided who have been sent to Hell. Unlike most
Bodhisattvas, he was usually depicted not as a gorgeously
ornamented deity, but as a simple monk with shaved head.
His only sign of extraordinary power is a jewel carried in
his left hand (here missing), which is emblematic of his
power to attain any material or spiritual goal.

Carved from a solid block of wood, this starkly simple
but powerfully conceived figure is most probably a provincial work. It also has the integrity of form and the
respect for the medium of wood which is a strong national
trait and is often found in Shinto sculpture of this period.
Similar methods of carving the folds over the legs and
making the pleats of the robe into simple bands may be
seen in figures from northern Honshū, as in a Kannon
figure at the Shōjō-ji in Fukushima prefecture of the late
ninth century (Takeshi Kuno, *Nihon no Chōkoku* [Vol. I,
Tōhoku], Tokyo, 1964, Pl. 6). The statue of Nāgārjuna
from the Ryūsen-in of Kōyasan is also similar in the handling of the diagonal draping of the robe across the body.
(J. Rosenfield, "Studies in Japanese Portraiture—the
statue of Nichira," *Oriental Art*, N.S. Vol. X [1964], p. 9,
Fig. 5). *Illus. p. 55.*

14 FLYING ANGEL
Tenth century
Wood; H. 18 in. (45.7 cm.), W. 18 in.
Capt. and Mrs. Roger Gerry, Roslyn

This rare and early example of a flying angel is carved in
low relief from a flat board. It shows a somewhat hesitant
effort to depict the body in motion, not so much through
anatomical detail as in the simple sweeping curves of the
garment and scarves. *Illus. p. 56.*

15 FLYING ANGEL
Second half of the eleventh century
Wood with traces of gesso and gold; H. 33½ in.
(85 cm.), W. 15 in. (38.1 cm.)
Museum of Fine Arts, Boston

Reputed to have come from the halo of an Amida image
at Kōfuku-ji in Nara, this work, an extremely mature and
sophisticated example of workshop production, was made
slightly after the time of Jōchō. Comparable in many ways
to the heavenly musicians and Bodhisattvas on the walls
of the Byōdō-in, it is carved with less surface detail but
with a stronger sense of plasticity and directed movement.
Illus. p. 20.

16 Zōchō-ten, Guardian of the South
Mid-ninth century
Wood with traces of gesso and color; H. 52¾ in.
(134 cm.)
Museum of Fine Arts, Boston; Ross Collection

In this image the stocky physique and sense of contained
fury belong to a sculptural style which developed in the
late eighth century in China and Japan. It may be con-
trasted with the taller, more elegant guardians in dry clay
of the mid-eighth century in the Kaidan-in of Tōdai-ji.

This statue is accompanied in the Boston Museum collection by a Bishamon-ten from the same original set of
four guardians. They are closely related to the Shitennō of
the East Kondō of Kōfuku-ji in Nara; resemblances are
strong in such details as the lion mask over the belt, the
proportions of the head and body, the pudgy demon
beneath his feet (*Kokuhō*, Vol. II, Pls. 7, 8). But in every
respect the Boston figures are simpler. They are less deeply
carved, and the masses of the body less skillfully disposed.
They are not provincial carvings, nor do they share the
extravagant movement and rage of the guardians of the
Tōji Lecture Hall in Kyoto, which may be slightly older.
Thus they are probably from a workshop in the Nara area
which was still free from the effects of the full Mikkyō
style and loyal to the style of wood carving associated with
the monasteries of Daian-ji and Tōshōdai-ji. *Illus. p. 57.*
Shown only at the Fogg Art Museum

17 Guardian General
Ca. early tenth century
Wood with thin lacquer coat and gold leaf; H.
(figure) 13¼ in. (33.6 cm.)
John G. Powers, New York

Said to come from Kōfuku-ji in Nara, this small figure
fits well into the stylistic sequence of the many statues of
guardians preserved at the temple. It must have been part
of a set of Twelve Guardian Generals, each of whom per-
sonifies a vow made by the Buddha Yakushi to heal mankind of its physical and spiritual ills. Kōfuku-ji has preserved a famous set of these figures, carved in very low
relief on wood panels three feet high (*Kokuhō*, Vol. III,
Pl. 60). The Powers statue is also conceived essentially in

low relief, although not as completely so as the others. It
shares their quality of whimsical humor but in a more
modified way, and thus may well be slightly earlier and
closer to the date of the Shitennō of the Eastern Kondō.
Note that the sleeves once flared much more fully around
the elbows. They have been broken and cut down, and
also several scarves which flowed down from the arms
have been lost. *Illus. p. 58.*

18 Standing Guardian
Late ninth or early tenth century
Wood; H. (figure) 37 in. (94 cm.).
John G. Powers, New York

The spontaneous and frightful wrath of guardian figures
of the early ninth century has abated somewhat in this
sculpture, which nonetheless retains the massive bulk of
the "Jōgan" style. It is related to an interesting group of
wooden figures done in a distinctive, local manner, having
very large heads and showing strong surface patterns in
the garment folds—the standing Kannon figures of Daigo-
ji and Onjō-ji of the mid-ninth century, for example
(*SBZS*, Vol. IV, figs. 46, 47). This guardian may be somewhat later, judged by the crisp undercutting around the
mouth and eyes and a larger volumetric unity in the entire
figure. *Illus. p. 59.*
Shown only at Asia House Gallery

19 Bishamon-ten, Guardian of the North
Ca. 1162
Woodblock print on paper; H. (figure) 6¹⁵⁄₁₆ in. (17.7
cm.)
Museum of Fine Arts, Boston; Gift of Robert Treat
Paine

Only a few among the large numbers of Buddhist prints
from the end of the Heian period may be precisely dated.
The earliest of these is a group of 100 sheets found inside a
handsome statue of Bishamon-ten in the Jōshin-in, a
Shingon temple in the Naka-no-kawa section of the
Yamato area. According to an accompanying inscription,

these images were inserted in 1162. As a rule, six figures were stamped individually on each sheet. This single figure in the collection of the Boston Museum is identical to those from the Jōshin-in and is probably from this group. *Illus. p. 60.*

Published: Ishida Mosaku *et al*, *Nihon Hanga Bijutsu Zenshū* (Vol. I, Kodai Hanga), Tokyo, 1961, pp. 159, 166, 167, Pl. 108; English translation and adaptation by Charles Terry, *Japanese Buddhist Prints*, Tokyo, 1964, No. 78; Takeshi Kuno, *Kantō Chōkoku no Kenkyū*, Tokyo, 1964, p. 317, No. 57; *SBZS*, Vol. V, Color Pl. 19.

20   HEAD OF GUARDIAN
     Last half of the eleventh century
     Assembled wood construction; H. 12½ in. (31.7 cm.)
     The Worcester Art Museum

The suave, markedly confident features of this guardian are extremely close to those of certain dated works of the late eleventh century: the Twelve Divine Generals of Kōryū-ji in Kyoto, of 1064 (*SBZS*, Vol. V, Pl. 43), or the Bishamon of the Kondō of Hōryū-ji, 1078. We may see it as a product of an atelier of the Heian capital and of the generation that followed Jōchō. *Illus. p. 61.*

21   STANDING BODHISATTVA
     First half of the eleventh century
     Cypress wood with traces of paint; H. (figure) 35¹³⁄₁₆ in. (91 cm.)
     John G. Powers, New York

Though working in the tradition of static, symmetrical figures carved from a single block of wood, the sculptor attempted to give this figure lightness and grace by bending the left knee slightly. He was anticipating the greater sense of motion and liveliness of Bodhisattva figures of the last half of the century. The flat, board halo is painted with a simple, decorative, floral pattern of considerable charm. The hands are later additions and seem to have been taken from a smaller image. *Illus. p. 62.*

Published: Kuno, *Kantō Chōkoku no Kenkyū*, Tokyo, 1964, p. 319, No. 60 (shown without the halo).

22   HEAD OF THE BUDDHA
     Mid-twelfth century
     Assembled wood construction; H. 14⅛ in. (35.9 cm.)
     Fogg Art Museum, Cambridge, Mass.; Gift of E. W. Forbes

Behind this tranquil and composed visage lie a thousand years of searching for the suitable expression of the almost contradictory properties of the Buddha: his severe wisdom and his compassion; his humanity and his superhuman powers. In its sense of lightness and discipline this head is a distinctly Japanese creation. A date of ca. 1150 is attested by close similarities to the slightly more sophisticated head of the Dainichi at Enjō-ji, carved by the youthful Unkei in 1176, with its inset crystal eyes and suggestions of fleshiness (Kuno, Pl. 79). *Illus. p. 63.*

23   HEAD AND TORSO OF BODHISATTVA
     Mid-twelfth century
     Assembled wood-block construction; H. 20¹³⁄₁₆ in. (53 cm.)
     John G. Powers, New York

This image is an example of the advanced wood-carving techniques developed by the sculptors of the metropolitan workshops of Kyoto and Nara after the time of Jochō. It is assembled of separate, thin pieces of wood like Nos. 4 and 22 above. The figure may originally have been in a seated position, for the waist retains traces of elements which would have supported the hips and legs.

A guide to the date of this piece is the well known statue of the Bodhisattva Fugen riding on his elephant, now in the Ōkura Museum, Tokyo, datable to the mid-twelfth century (Bunsaku Kurata, *Butsuzō no mikata*, Tokyo, 1965, pp. 204–209; Sherwood Moran, "The Statue of Fugen Bosatsu, Ōkura Museum, Tokyo," *Ars Asiatiques*, VII [1960], pp. 287–310). The Tokyo figure retains much of its original coating of lacquer and paint, now missing from the Powers Bodhisattva, but in proportion and in a pervasive mood of gentleness and composure the two works are closely comparable. *Illus. p. 64.*

Published: Mayuyama, No. 36.

24 SEATED YAKUSHI

Second half of the twelfth century
Cast bronze; H. 10¾ in. (27.3 cm.), w. 8 in. (20.3 cm.)
Mr. and Mrs. John D. Rockefeller 3rd, New York

The making of statues in bronze, a favored medium during the early phases of Buddhist art in Japan in the seventh and eighth centuries, was resumed in the latter half of the Heian period. Bronze afforded permanence for images buried in the Sutra Mounds; it may also have served the growing taste for the revival of old religious and artistic values. This small figure of the Healing Buddha is faithful to the Jōchō style in its advanced stage of development, but a distinct archaistic reserve is present—in the stiffly erect pose, the narrowing of the chest, and the severely plain surfaces. The treatment of the garment folds is comparable to that of the Amida from Mitaki-dera in Hiroshima, for example, dated 1154 (*SBZS*, Vol. V, Pl. 61), but the proportions of the eyes and nose indicate a somewhat later date. *Illus. p. 65.*

25 GODDESS BENZAI-TEN PLAYING A LUTE

Late twelfth century
Color on silk; H. 47½ in. (120.7 cm.), w. 27 in. (68.5 cm.)
Nelson Gallery—Atkins Museum, Kansas City, Mo.

Placed on a rocky promontory beside a low waterfall is Benzai-ten, the goddess of learning, the fine arts, and prosperity. She sits in the Indian "position of royal ease" with her shoes on the ground before her, her right leg resting on the ground, and the back of the biwa (lute) against her left knee.

The door paintings of the shrine of the Goddess Kichi-jō-ten from Jōruri-ji near Nara (*Bijutsu Kenkyū* [Oct., 1939], No. 94) serve as a guide to the date of this work. The goddesses depicted there and believed to date from before 1212 wear costumes with jewelled yokes which are almost identical to that of Benzai-ten, and the drawing of their facial features is also similar, though the execution and coloring are considerably more coarse. The door paintings are overtly archaistic in spirit; some were actually based on tracings of Nara period designs. Archaistic also is the goddess in this painting, for she sits beneath a blossoming tree in a manner reminiscent of the woman-and-tree screens of the Shōsō-in collection.

This painting dates from a period of transition between late Heian and Kamakura styles, hence it is difficult to give a precise date, but in its soft tonality, the delicacy of workmanship, and the taut, disciplined facial features, the flavor of late Heian painting may still be felt.

On the lute's plectrum guard is a scene of a tiger, full moon and clouds, a landscape motif which recurs in the many later versions of this theme (see *Kokka*, Nos. 314, 473, 724). The cult of the goddess increased in appeal through the Kamakura period for she was given a secure place in the Shinto pantheon, returning thus to a pagan status which was hers originally in India as the Hindu goddess Sarasvatī. *Illus. p. 66.*

Published: Mayuyama, No. 86; Lee, Nos. 18, 136; *Handbook Nelson Gallery of Art—Atkins Museum*, Fourth Ed., Kansas City, Mo., 1959, p. 215; Langdon Warner, *The Enduring Art of Japan*, Cambridge, Mass., 1952, fig. 19.

26 CINERARY URN WITH PARADISE SCENES

Early Heian period
Gilt bronze; H. 9¾ in. (24.7 cm.)
The Cleveland Museum of Art; purchase from the J. H. Wade Fund

This gilded bronze vessel was probably made as a receptacle for the cremated remains of a person of high standing. In the upper register are engraved no less than four heavenly scenes. One shows a Buddha beneath a canopy, flanked by Bodhisattvas and small pagodas; approaching on either side are triads of praying Buddhas and Bodhisattvas on flowing clouds. A second scene is dominated by an octagonal hall like the Yumedono of Hōryū-ji, surrounded by four smaller buildings. It is approached by large, flying figures without halos. On either side of this scene are groups of cloud-borne palaces or temple buildings.

Each of these four heavenly scenes is linked by cloud trails to the lower register, which may depict the everyday world. Shown in a loose, scattered mode of composition are a wild beast chasing a tiny man and a rabbit; men riding on fabulous beasts; and pheasants, pigeons, and cranes (one of which carries a man) which seem to be rising toward heaven. The composition recalls the more complex, incised designs on the Baptismal Bowl for the small, bronze, Nara period image of Śākyamuni at Tōdai-ji (*Kokuhō*, Vol. I, Pl. 82). The architectural elements shown here are of the eighth century, but the fabric of this vessel and its proportions suggest a date well into the ninth. The lid may be a later replacement of a lost original. *Illus. p. 72.*

Published: Lee, No. 12.

27 SEATED AMIDA BUDDHA
Late eleventh–early twelfth century
Polychromed wood; H. 32 in. (81.3 cm.)
Mr. and Mrs. Jackson Burke, New York

According to Kuno, this piece may well have been carved in a Nara workshop which had come under the influence of the style and technique of Jōchō (died 1057). But even though this piece is imbued with an air of alert discipline, it lacks the mathematical precision and sharpness of the Jōchō style as seen in the Byōdō-in Amida (Fig. 6, p. 31). It resembles a number of works found chiefly in Nara and adjacent prefectures; for example, the image of Yakushi Nyorai in the Fukuhara-dera, Yoshino, dated 1085 (*Museum,* No. 155, [December, 1964], p. 27).

The pedestal, painted with blue-green and cinnabar red, is probably original. Inside the pedestal are written the characters for *Terai*; hence the image may have come from the Dainichi-dō, Terai, Koga-gun, Shiga prefecture.

The surface color of the statue itself appears to be original, and the dark stripes of the robe create a patchwork pattern, a reflection of ancient Indian Buddhist monastic apparel. The hand gesture, the *Jōbon geshō-in,* is the one most often seen in small, seated Amida images and is symbolic of the Buddha Amida's welcome to virtuous men entering the third division of the upper sector of Paradise. *Illus. p. 67.*

Published: Takeshi Kuno, "Shui kintai no Amida Nyoraizō (Amida image with a cinnabar-colored robe and gilded body)," *Kobijutsu,* No. 1 (1963), pp. 75–80.

28 FRAGMENT OF SCENE OF AMIDA'S PARADISE
Late Heian period
Lacquer on wood; H. 3 1/16 in. (7.7 cm.), W. 5 3/16 in. (13.2 cm.)
The Cleveland Museum of Art; John L. Severance Fund

This fragment taken from a large scene of the Western

Paradise shows the corridors and pavilions which surround the Palace of Amida—structures which resemble parts of the Phoenix Hall of the Byōdō-in at Uji (Fig. 5, p. 28). Visible here are musicians and Bodhisattvas who attend Amida's court. The design is built up of granulated gold and silver in a technique called *maki-e.* This fragment is mounted as the lid of a box, as is another section of the same composition in the Boston Museum. *Illus. p. 73.*

Published: Mayuyama, No. 308; Lee, No. 6.

29 ONE HUNDRED IMAGES OF AMIDA NYORAI
Early twelfth century
Woodblock print on paper; H. 17 3/8 in. (44.2 cm.), W. 12 3/4 in. (32.4 cm.)
Mr. and Mrs. Money Hickman, Cambridge, Mass.

The Main Hall (Hondō) of Jōruri-ji, a temple situated in the low mountains east of Nara, houses a notable group of nine statues of the Buddha Amida. During restoration work on the central image of this group some years ago, many sheets of woodblock prints, among them the one shown here, were discovered inside the statue. The pages were printed with rows of small Amida figures, each seated in meditation. In this example one hundred images printed from a single block of wood are arranged in ten horizontal rows.

Although printing had been practiced in Japan as early as the eighth century, the stamping or block printing of large numbers of Buddhist images did not gain prominence until the last half of the Heian period. The repetition of images was believed to be an effective method of accumulating religious merit, and this stimulated the production of Buddhist prints—often rather crudely made—in vast numbers. The blocks or stamps most commonly used contained anywhere from a single image up to a dozen identical units; large full-sheet blocks, such as this one, seem to have been used much less frequently. *Illus. p. 74.*

Published: Mosaku *et al, Nihon Hanga Bijutsu Zenshū,* Vol. I, Pls. 44, 45; Terry, *Japanese Buddhist Prints,* Pl. 78.

30 STANDING IMAGES OF SHŌ KANNON
Twelfth century
Wood with traces of color; average height of figures 15 1/4 in. (38.7 cm.), of pedestals 3 3/4 in. (9.5 cm.)

a. John G. Powers, New York
b. John G. Powers, New York
c. Mr. and Mrs. Jackson Burke, New York
d. Capt. and Mrs. Roger Gerry, Roslyn
e. The Brooklyn Museum, New York
f. Fogg Art Museum, Cambridge, Mass.

It is believed that a large altar or special hall designed for a thousand images of Kannon once stood within the precincts of Kōfuku-ji, the Fujiwara family temple in Nara. The five figures assembled here are said to have come from this temple. The custom of building a Sentai Butsu-dō (Hall of the Thousand Buddhas) became widespread in the twelfth century; the chief relic standing today, however, is the Sanjūsangen-dō in Kyoto, reconstructed in the 1250's on the site of the hall founded by the Emperor Goshirakawa in 1164. The images from Kōfuku-ji are much smaller than those of Kyoto, and they are much more varied in pose, proportion, and costume. Fifty examples are in the Fujita Museum, Osaka (*Catalogue, Tenth Anniversary Exhibition*, 1964, p. 18). *Illus. pp. 68–71.*

f. *shown only at the Fogg Art Museum*

31 PROCESSIONAL MASKS
Late tenth–early eleventh century
Wood with traces of lacquer and color
a. One of the Jūni-ten
   H. 11 in. (27.9 cm.), w. 6¾ in. (17.2 cm.)
b. Bodhisattva Mask
   H. 8¼ in. (20.9 cm.), w. 6⅞ in. (17.5 cm.)
Honolulu Academy of Arts

Preserved at Tōji in Kyoto are seven masks from an original set of twelve depicting the Jūni-ten, the Twelve Guardian Deities (see No. 7 above). Inscriptions on each state that they were repaired in 1186 and again in 1334, and, on the basis of temple records, they may have been in the temple at the very beginning of the eleventh century, along with nineteen others. (See *Tōji*, Tokyo: Asahi Shimbun-sha, 1956, Figs. 57–62.) The masks shown here are said to have come from Tōji.

Except for the loss of much of the old surface pigment and undercoat, the mask of one of the Jūni-ten (a.) closely resembles the remaining seven of the original set. Of the

five masks which are now missing from Tōji, only that of Rasetsu-ten (Rakshasa) would be as demonic as this one, with his bulging eyes and protruding teeth. *Illus. p. 75.*

The second mask (b.) also agrees closely with the style of the seven remaining in Tōji, except that it lacks the ornate headdress which is common to them all. It may thus be a Bodhisattva and may be from the set of nineteen masks also recorded as once having been in the temple. The left side of the face and ear have been restored. *Illus. p. 78.*

Published: Mayuyama, No. 41.

32 PROCESSIONAL MASK
Late tenth–early eleventh century
Wood with traces of lacquer; H. 9¼ in. (23.5 cm.)
John G. Powers, New York

Differing only in matters of small detail (the opening for the eyes, the ridge behind the crown) from No. 31 b. above, this mask may be of roughly the same vintage. It is likely that these masks were worn in processions which, with the beating of drums and sounding of flutes and chanting of prayers, recreated the Raikō of Amida—the coming of the Buddha and an entourage of Bodhisattvas and musicians to receive the soul of a dying man. Called the Mukae-kō, the custom is still maintained at a few temples, such as Taima-dera south of Nara and Nembutsu-ji to the west of Kyoto. *Illus. p. 76.*

Published: Mayuyama, No. 45.

33 PROCESSIONAL MASK
Mid-twelfth century
Wood, lacquered and painted; H. 8⅝ in. (21.9 cm.)
The Cleveland Museum of Art; John L. Severance Fund

Compared to the Tōji masks, this example is considerably more delicate and refined—the bridge of its nose is narrower, the eyes smaller, the eyebrows cut through the wood. Like the Buddha and Bodhisattva figures of the same date (Nos. 22 and 23 above), it has affinities to the early style of Unkei. *Illus. p. 77.*

Published: Mayuyama, No. 42; *Bulletin of the Cleveland Museum of Art*, XXXVIII (Nov. 1951), p. 212.

34 ILLUMINATED SUTRAS FROM CHŪSON-JI
Mid-twelfth century
Gold and silver ink on indigo paper; frontispieces H.
10⅟₁₆ in. (25.6 cm.), w. 8⅛ in. (20.7 cm.)
a. *Daihanyaharamita-kyō* (*Mahāprajñāpāramitā-sūtra*),
  Vol. 338
The New York Public Library; Spencer Collection
b. *Daihanyaharamita-kyo*, Vol. 582
John G. Powers, New York

A branch of the Fujiwara family ruled, virtually independently, the northern quarter of Honshū Island. After
the discovery of gold in the late eleventh century, their
wealth increased and the temples which they built in their
capital at Hiraizumi rivaled in splendor those of their dis-
tant relatives in the Heian Kyō. Three generations of
northern Fujiwaras donated to Chūson-ji, their tutelary
temple, a hand-copied set of parts of the vast body of
Buddhist canonical texts, the *Issaikyō*. Today 2,739 scrolls
remain in the Sutra Storage there; 4,296 scrolls were trans-
ferred to Kongōbu-ji on Kōyasan in the late sixteenth
century; others are found in Kanshin-ji and in numerous
private collections.

This immense project began around 1117 and stopped
in 1176, as the northern Fujiwaras, embroiled in the rival-
ries between the Tairas and Minamotos, earned the enmity
of the latter, who eventually destroyed their power. The
majority of the extant scrolls at Chūson-ji were done
during the rule of the second major leader, Fujiwara
Motohira (died 1157), and were painted by as many as ten
different hands. They vary in style and subject from stiff,
hieratic views of the Buddhist pantheon to narrative scenes
with a strong secular flavor, and even purely decorative
landscape compositions with no ideological content.
(*Kokuhō*, Vol. III, Nos. 110, 111.)

In the Spencer Collection sutra (a.) an enthroned
Buddha, Bodhisattvas, and monks seem to have appeared
in the world to intervene in a conflict between four armed
soldiers and three men or boys. A Bodhisattva is offering
something, apparently to placate the warriors. This
crowded, active composition fits into the stylistic context
of the frontispiece to volumes 335, 336 (*Chūson-ji Ōkagami*,
Tokyo, 1941, Pl. 52). *Illus. p. 80.*

The Powers manuscript (b.) shows an enthroned
Buddha, accompanied by Bodhisattvas and monks, seated
in a landscape before a two-storied Buddhist temple build-

ing. For volumes 578 and 585, see *Chūson-ji Ōkagami*, Pl.
62. *Illus. p. 81.*

35 FRONTISPIECE OF ILLUMINATED SUTRA
Mid-twelfth century
Gold and silver ink on indigo paper; H. 10¾ in. (27.3
cm.), w. 10⁹⁄₁₆ in. (26.9 cm.)
Anonymous loan

This frontispiece, detached from the sutra scroll itself, is
identical in style and composition with one preserved at
Enryaku-ji (*Hiei-zan Enryaku-ji sōkan* [Ōtsu city, 1955],
Pl. 57). Both are remarkable for their relatively high
quality of draftsmanship and execution—a rough vigor
in the cloud forms and trees, a decisiveness in figure painting unusual in sutra frontispieces, which so often were
given over to repetitive formulae. There is a very strong
degree of Chinese influence in the style and in details of
costume. *Illus. p. 79.*

36 ILLUMINATED SUTRA FROM JINGO-JI
Last half twelfth century
Gold and silver ink on blue paper; frontispiece H.
10⅟₁₆ in. (25.6 cm.), w. 8⅝ in. (22 cm.)
John G. Powers, New York

To the monastery of Jingo-ji the Imperial Family donated
a large set of illuminated sutra scrolls. The project was
begun by the Retired Emperor Toba just before his death
in 1156, and was continued through the time of the Emperor Goshirakawa, who actually lived at Jingo-ji after he
abdicated the throne in 1158. The set from which this
sutra comes is believed to have comprised over 2,500 scrolls,
but unlike the Chūson-ji sutras their frontispieces were not
varied. These repeat the single theme of a seated Buddha
flanked by monks and Bodhisattvas; in the background is
the peak of a mountain shaped like the head of a bird, an
allusion to the Vulture Peak near Rājagriha in India, upon
which Śākyamuni was said to have delivered the Lotus
Sūtra and a number of other Mahāyāna texts. The name
of this scroll is written *Daichi-ron*, a short form for *Daichido-
ron* (*Mahāprajñā-pāramitopadeśa*), and it bears the Jingo-ji
seal. *Illus. p. 82.*

37 PAGES FROM THE COLLECTION OF THE THIRTY-SIX
POETS (*Sanjūroku-nin shū*)

Early twelfth century

Ink on ornamented paper; each single sheet approximately H. 7¹⁵⁄₁₆ in. (20.1 cm.), w. 6¼ in. (15.9 cm.)

a. Mr. Saburo Hiraki, Tokyo

b. Seattle Art Museum; Eugene Fuller Memorial
Collection

c. Philadelphia Museum of Art

d. Mr. and Mrs. Jackson Burke, New York

The taste of the Heian courtiers and their fondness for
poetry are perhaps nowhere better revealed than in the
Sanjūroku-nin shū, a sumptuous anthology of the works of
thirty-six poets. Of the original set, thirty-four books containing 2,700 pages in a great variety of decorated papers
survived intact into modern times. Some sheets were made
by a collage method of tearing (*yaburi-tsugi*) or cutting
(*kiri-tsugi*) colored papers and combining them in bold
designs; other pages are composites made of small colored
pieces of paper, carefully glued together. On others, woodblock designs were printed with an ink made of ground
mica and impressed onto a thin gesso primer, to provide a
shimmering and lustrous writing surface. The sheets were
folded down the middle and pasted to the adjacent sheets
at each fold. No thread was used to bind the books.

Twenty calligraphers, mainly of aristocratic lineage,
worked on the project. They included Fujiwara Sadanobu
(1089–1152 [?]), one of Japan's most distinguished masters
of this art, and Fujiwara Michiko, who died in 1132, a
woman of very high rank who served the Retired Emperor
Shirakawa. The script used was the cursive *Sōgana*, a distinctly Japanese writing style using mostly the flowing
letters of the native *Hiragana* syllabary and relatively few
Chinese characters.

The collection remained in the possession of the Imperial
Household until 1549, when the Emperor Gonara presented it to the Hongan-ji in Kyoto. In 1929 the temple sold
one volume of the poems of Ki no Tsurayuki and one of
the poetess Ise. These two volumes comprise the so-called
Ishiyama-gire (-fragment), named after Ishiyama, the
original location of Hongan-ji (in Osaka).

a. DOUBLE PAGE FROM THE COLLECTED POEMS OF
TSURAYUKI

Kino Tsurayuki (884[?]–946) served as a government
official and was also a poet of great renown. At the order of
the Emperor Daigo, for example, he joined with others in
compiling the *Kokinshū*, an anthology of ancient and contemporary Japanese poems. Tsurayuki's preface to this is
an historic statement of the ideals of Japanese poetry, of its
lyrical and gentle spirit. His own work is considered very
courtly, filled with decorous elegance in its diction and
poetic organization.

This double page of his poems in the Hiraki collection,
Tokyo, is distinguished by a bold collage design of a dark
blue river flowing from top to bottom on the right half.
Made from roughly torn paper, it is as boldly and arbitrarily conceived as any design by the later masters of
decorative schools, such as Sōtatsu or Kōrin.

To the extreme right is a large floral and lozenge pattern
in printed mica, over which is written the following prose
preface:

> *Poetry collection of Commander Ki. Number 10. Miscellaneous. Composed on the subject of flowers painted on a
> folding screen:*

Written in slanting lines through the dark water is the
following poem:

> *Springtime must have ruled*
> *The earth continuously*
> *Since their first flowering*
> *For their color never fades!*

A strip of paper with cloud-like coloring was once pasted
over the water as a flap which could be lifted (traces of the
glue may still be seen near the top of the sheet). Now
mounted separately, it contains the text of the poem as
written on the water, identical except for a copyist's error,
and seems to date from about the time of the original version. Two such strips were found pasted over pages of the
Sanjūroku-nin shū: this one repeats a passage which is difficult to read, and another adds a passage which had been
omitted.

The text of the left hand page is written over a floral
design in printed mica. The preface states:

> *On being asked by a certain person to compose a poem on
> the line "Night clouds have disappeared; the moon moves
> slowly":*

The poem may be translated:

The long cloud-layers
Trailed across the sky have left
No trace upon the night:
Light of the voyaging moon
Bathes the scene with tranquil radiance.

The preface of the next poem states:

Composed when Ōshikōchi no Mitsune (active ca. 900, a
court poet and colleague of Tsurayuki) came to visit one
night of pleasant moonlight:

The poem:

Together we admire
This moonlit night; and yet I feel
Your friendship is but cool,
For like the moon you shed
Your favor on all men impartially.

Illus. p. 34.
Published: Shimbi Tanaka, (*Nishihon*) *Sanjūroku-nin shū*,
Tokyo, 1960, p. 29; see also Utsubo Kubota, *Kokinwakashū*
Hyōshaku, Tokyo, 1960.
Shown only at Asia House Gallery

b. PAGE FROM THE COLLECTED POEMS OF TSURAYUKI

The Seattle Art Museum's page from the Ishiyama-gire
has poems by Ki no Tsurayuki written over a floral and
lozenge pattern printed in silver and gray inks. The preface
states:

Added to a gift of a fan sent to the Governor of Chikugo on
his departure from the capital:

The poem may be tentatively translated:

A wind that will never fail
Though you were to fan forever
Such is my deep respect for you.

The poem contains a word-play on *ogi* (*aogi*), which means
"fan" as well as "respect." Hence the third line can also be
rendered "This is the fan (I give to you)."

The preface to the next poem indicates that the poem
was added to a gift of apparel and *nusa* (pieces of paper or
cloth used as offerings for safety on a journey) sent to the
daughter of Fujiwara no Okikata, Governor of Owari, on
her departure from the capital. The poem itself may be
tentatively translated:

These paper offerings
For the starting of your journey
May the gods accept,
And these my loving thoughts report to you,
At every shrine along the spear-straight way.

Illus. p. 84.
Published: *Japanese Art in the Seattle Art Museum*, 1960, No·
41; Mayuyama, No. 300; Lee, No. 20.

c. PAGE FROM THE COLLECTED POEMS OF ISE

Another page of the Ishiyama-gire, from the Philadelphia Museum of Art, contains poems by Ise no Go (died
ca. 940), consort of the Emperor Uda. Lacking annotated
and edited texts, only a tentative translation may be offered.
The first line is a continuation of a poem on the previous
page:

. . . why should I have thought it a lie?

The preface to the following poem indicates that it is a
response to a note proposing that the poetess' young son
be married to the other person's daughter. The poem reads:

Sad would it be
If from a moment's meeting
Came one-sided love.

The preface to the next poem indicates that it was composed on the occasion of the Tanabata Festival (on the
seventh day of the seventh month, often observed by
young women hoping for faithful husbands).

Were there no
Reminder of your being
In the features of this child,
Forgetfulness might come.

Illus. p. 85.
Published: Mayuyama, No. 301.

d. PAGE FROM THE COLLECTED POEMS OF ISE

Also from the Collected Poems of Ise no Go (the *Ise Shū*)
is a page in the collection of Mr. and Mrs. Jackson Burke.
Written by the same hand as the Philadelphia Museum
page, the text appears over a printed design of boldly
abstract floral shapes in an ink of ground mica, lustrous
and subtle in effect. Pale gold ink was used for the scattered
motifs of flying geese, wind-blown flowers, and tree
branches of willow, pine, wisteria, and plum. The first line
is a continuation of a poem on the previous page:

. . . the color has deepened.

The preface to the next two poems, a witty repartee between an amorous man and a reluctant lady, states:

> *The man came and stood at her gate; hearing a cuckoo singing in a flowering orange tree, he composed the following verse and sent it in to the lady:*

> *Standing at your gate*
> *Forlorn am I as the mournful*
> *Cuckoo that sings*
> *My sadness from his perch among*
> *The branches of your blossoming orange tree.*

To this she replied:

> *Hardly can he know*
> *What errand brings you here,*
> *The cuckoo in my tree—*
> *Is it not his tuneful nature*
> *Thus to come and sing?*

Illus. p. 83.

Translations by Edwin A. and Fumiko Cranston

38 SECTION FROM THE "MENASHI-GYŌ"
Text inscribed in 1193; painting done ca. 1160–1170
Ink on paper with flecks of silver leaf on back, guide lines drawn in silver; H. 10¾ in. (27.3 cm.), w. 8⅛ in. (20.7 cm.)
Anonymous loan

A major project in narrative painting comprising possibly five handscrolls, each ranging up to thirty feet in length, seems to have been commissioned by the Retired Emperor Goshirakawa. The artists had barely outlined their compositions and had not yet begun to apply color when, for some reason, the project was stopped and the scrolls were given by the Emperor to a loyal nun called Zenni. When the Emperor died in 1192 the descendants of the nun, for the sake of the souls of both nun and Emperor, had two distinguished monk calligraphers inscribe over the paintings the texts of three important Mahāyāna sutras, the Lotus (*Hokke-kyō*), the *Suvarnaprabhāsa* and the *Prajñāpāramitā*. Most of the work has been cut apart and redistributed; only one scroll remains intact. (*Kokuhō*, Vol. V, Nos. 60, 61.)

The subjects illustrated were taken from a variety of literary sources, most of which are unidentified. However, they include scenes from the *Genji Monogatari* and seem to feature tales of horror and demon possession. The drawings are done in a style close to that of the oldest extant illustrations of the *Genji Monogatari* (now in the Tokugawa and Gotō collections). Interior scenes are shown as though seen from above in a ceilingless room; the faces are drawn only in a schematic, undetailed manner (hence the nickname, the "menashi," or "eyeless" sutras); probably the colors were to have been applied in strong, opaque pigments.

This fragment shows a young woman kneeling on what appear to be mats; a small child stands at an open doorway and gesticulates with a long stick. Of special interest is the fact that the implied vantage point of the spectator seems to be inside the room looking out.

The history of this project as outlined above must be somewhat speculative for parts of the colophon inscription have been lost. A variant explanation holds that the painting was being done jointly by the Retired Emperor and the nun when the former died and the work was left unfinished. Akiyama, however, suggests convincingly that Zenni died long before Goshirakawa.

See: Yoshi Shirahata, "Menashi-gyō ni tsuite," *Bijutsu Kenkyū* (September, 1940), No. 105, pp. 264–277; Terukazu Akiyama, *Heian Jidai Sezokuga no Kenkyū*, Tokyo, 1964, pp. 279–299.

Illus. pp. 86, 87.

39 YAKUSHU-SHŌ (MATERIA MEDICA) BY KENI AJARI
Late twelfth century
Book form; H. 6⅝ in. (16.8 cm.), w. 5¹¹⁄₁₆ in. (14. 5cm.)
Anonymous loan

Illustrated with thirty-one pages of ink drawings, this book from Kōzan-ji in Kyoto is an account of aromatic herbs of the Chinese pharmacopoeia to be burned in the Esoteric Goma ritual. The author, a member of the Fujiwara clan known as Keni Ajari, was active from 1095 to 1156 as a writer and theologian. The manuscript was copied by two separate but unknown hands, and the drawings have a lucidity and clarity of conception which was a characteristic of late Heian period draftsmanship. Even though the illustrator was not a professional, his illustrations approach the threshold of expressive imagery.

The identical text and drawings of the same period in scroll form have been preserved at Ishiyama-dera. (J. Takakusu and G. Ono, *Taishō Shinshū Daizōkyō Zuzō*, Tokyo, 1934, Vol. XI, pp. 177–230.) This book bears the seal of the Hōbenchi-in, a sub-temple of Kōzan-ji. *Illus. p. 90.*

40 TREATISE ON MEDICINES AND INCENSE BY SHOKEN
Mid-twelfth century
Handscroll, ink on paper; section with illustrations,
H. 11 in. (27.9 cm.), L. 30½ in. (77.5 cm.)
The New York Public Library; Spencer Collection

In this handscroll, a treatise on medicines and incense, the illustrations follow processionally one upon another, uninterrupted by the text. The author was the monk Shōken (1138–1196), eighteenth Abbot of Daigo-ji and a prolific writer on liturgical and semi-scientific subjects. The section illustrated here shows sources of incense, such as the musk ox and magnolias from various provinces. Illustrations virtually the same in style and detail appear in a scroll preserved at Ishiyama-dera. In this other, however, they are interspersed with the text, which is attributed to the monk Keni Ajari, also of Daigo-ji (see No. 39 above; also Takakusu and Ono, *Taishō Shinshū Daizōkyō Zuzō*, Vol. XI, pp. 71–176). The Spencer Collection scroll is one of a set of three in a box bearing a date of 1165; one of the others also deals with incense, and one with jewels and metals. *Illus. pp. 88, 89.*

41 ALMS BOWL
Tenth century
Gilt bronze; H. 5 in. (12.7 cm.), diam. 9⅜ in. (23.8 cm.)
The Cleveland Museum of Art; Purchase from the J. H. Wade Fund

Although monasticism remained the prime form of Buddhist discipline during the Heian period, the monks' furnishings—robes, walking staffs, incense burners, and even begging bowls—became increasingly ornate. This gilded vessel was intended to serve as an alms bowl to be filled with food given by laymen to a mendicant monk, but with its rich gilding and engraved butterflies and flowers it has an aristocratic flavor. The design is not greatly different from that on the Nyo-i (teaching baton)

of Daigo-ji, which is more sharply engraved and is perhaps slightly later in date. *Illus. p. 92.*
Published: *Bulletin of The Cleveland Museum of Art*, XXXVIII (Nov., 1951), p. 212.

42 HEAD OF MONK'S STAFF
Late twelfth century
Cast bronze; H. 9¼ in. (24.7 cm.), w. (max.) 5⅝ in. (14.3 cm.)
Peabody Museum, Salem; Gift of C. G. Weld

A staff was one of the eighteen items of personal property a Buddhist monk was allowed to own. Usually equipped with metal rings which rang as he walked (missing here), the staff served to warn insects away from his path, to announce his coming to householders who would give him alms, and also to beat the rhythm of a chant.
This unusual example bears identical, cast images, placed back to back. In the center is a Bodhisattva holding a flask, his head encircled with a flaming halo. Flanking him are two guardian Niō (Benevolent Kings). On the outer ring are a monk and a layman in gestures of prayer, and three small pagodas. The general style and fabric of the work are somewhat rough and suggest the time of transition between the late Heian and Kamakura periods; an almost identical example is in the Nezu Collection. (*Illustrated Catalogue of Famous Masterpieces in the Collection of the Nezu Art Museum*, Tokyo, 1955, No. 238.) *Illus. p. 91.*

43 MIRROR WITH DESIGN OF TWO BIRDS AND FLOWERS
Twelfth century
Bronze; diam. 5¼ in. (13.3 cm.)
The Avery Brundage Foundation, M. H. De Young Memorial Museum, San Francisco

This beautifully preserved eight-lobed mirror shows the persistence of T'ang Chinese-style decorative elements in the two small ducks and flowers. *Illus. p. 93.*

44 MIRROR WITH DESIGN OF CRANES AND PINE NEEDLES
Ca. eleventh–twelfth century
Cast bronze; diam. 4⅛ in. (10.4 cm.)
Museum of Fine Arts, Boston

A pair of cranes flying among falling needles is deftly shown in low relief on this mirror. The flat surface of the mirror was originally silvered. Cranes and pine trees are among the many emblems of longevity in the Sino-Japanese language of nature symbolism, and mirrors of the late Heian period bearing this motif have been excavated throughout Japan in great numbers. Usually, they were given by laymen for deposit in Sutra Mounds or for use in similar rituals.

This mirror, together with No. 45 below, is said to have been one of more than two hundred which were recovered from Mitarashi Pond, a small lake in front of a shrine now called Haguro Jinja, atop Mount Haguro in the Asahi-Bandai National Park. Mount Haguro is the central peak of three mountains which were climbed by Buddhist monks and laymen who followed the practices of the Yama Busshi, or Shūgen-sha. These ascetics likened the ascent of the mountain, in a slow, arduous, ceremonial fashion, to the process of withdrawal from the ordinary world of human affairs in order to reach the summit of spiritual achievement. Apparently these mirrors were thrown into the lake at the end of the ascent by the hundreds of people who took part in the ritual. (See *Haguro-yama kokagami zufu*, Yamagata prefecture, 1934.) *Illus. p. 94.*

45 Mirror with Design of Sparrows and Chrys-anthemums
Ca. eleventh–twelfth century
Cast bronze; diam. 3⅝ in. (9.1 cm.)
Museum of Fine Arts, Boston

Like No. 44 above, this mirror is said to have come from the pond before the Haguro Shrine atop Mount Haguro. *Illus. p. 95.*

46 Mirror with Design of Cranes and Pine Needles
Eleventh–twelfth century
Cast bronze; diam. 3³⁄₁₆ in. (8.1 cm.)
The Avery Brundage Foundation, M. H. De Young Memorial Museum, San Francisco

This version of an extremely popular design also shows

flying cranes holding pine needles in their beaks. This piece, though similar to the Boston Museum mirror from Mount Haguro (No. 44), is from an unknown site, but its patina indicates that probably it was excavated from a Sutra Mound. Similar examples have been found at the Sutra Mound of Kimpuzen, and elsewhere throughout the Empire (*Kimpuzen*, Pls. 58.1, 104.1, 104.5; Osamu Kurata, "Kyōzuka-ron," *Museum*, No. 147 [June, 1963], p. 2, ff.) *Illus. p. 95.*

47 Mirror with Design of Reeds or Grass
Late Heian period
Cast bronze; diam. 3½ in. (8.9 cm.)
The Avery Brundage Foundation, M. H. De Young Memorial Museum, San Francisco

In its subtle design, in low relief, this is a clear example of the austere and evocative native Japanese style of mirror, the *wa-gyō*. *Illus. p. 96.*

48 Mirror with Engraved Design of Zaō Gongen
Eleventh–twelfth century
Copper alloy; diam. 9¹¹⁄₁₆ in. (24.5 cm.)
Harold P. Stern, Washington, D.C.

This mirror from Kimpuzen-ji, Yoshino district, Nara prefecture, shows Zaō Gongen striding to his right, his right foot upraised and a one-pronged thunderbolt brandished close to his head. His left hand, held at the hip, has two fingers pointing stiffly out in the *ken-in* ("sword gesture"). The left foot stands on a rocky, crag-like form. His headdress is adorned with floral shapes, and the locks of his hair stream upward as though moved by the energy of his wrath.

Mount Kimpu in the Yoshino district forms part of the mountain boundary which encloses the eastern end of the ancient Yamato country. Originally Zaō Gongen must have been the chief of the animistic Shinto gods who dwelled on the mountain. He was given a place in the Buddhist pantheon through the doctrines of Ryōbu Shinto whereby native Japanese gods were considered avatars (*gongen* or *keshin*) of Buddhist deities. Zaō is said to be an incarnation of no less than three major Buddhist figures: chiefly Maitreya, the messianic Buddha of the future, but also Śākyamuni and Avalokiteśvara.

Images of Zaō were conceived in the manner of such Tantric Buddhist forms as the Myō-ō (the Vīdyarājas, or Bright Kings)—given three eyes, engulfed in flames, grimacing with fiercely expressive faces, and holding the thunderbolt (*vajra* or *kongō*) so common in Esoteric Buddhist symbolism. As a giver of wealth and protector of the faithful, Zaō came to be worshipped throughout the country; but the center of his cult remained atop Mount Kimpu, where scores of his images were excavated in the Sutra Mound next to the Main Hall of Kimpuzen-ji.

This mirror was formed by joining two thin sheets of copper alloy, the front folded and bent over the back. The surface was originally silvered and polished. A small, square hole probably served for attaching the mirror to a wall. *Illus. p. 97.*

Published: *Kimpuzen*, Fig. 21.1, Pl. 63.2, p. 118.

49 ZAŌ GONGEN
Eleventh–twelfth century
Bronze plaque; H. 15½ in. (39.35 cm.), w. 9 in. (22.9 cm.)
Fogg Art Museum, Cambridge, Mass.; Gift of Meta and Paul Sachs in memory of Langdon Warner

A rather genial air pervades this figure of Zaō, the wrathful energies of early Heian period Esoteric Buddhist imagery having been tempered by the passage of time. The older spirit is preserved in No. 48 above, and the figure on this thin, bronze plaque is iconographically similar to that on the mirror except for the different form of his thunderbolt. The plaque has a green patination. Although the Fogg example is not included among its published relics, the Kimpuzen Sutra Mound is the most likely source of the plaque; very similar objects, also in cast bronze, were found there. (*Kimpuzen*, Pls. 47, 50, 81, 82.) *Illus. p. 98.*

Published: *Exhibition of Japanese Buddhistic Art*, Yamanaka and Company, Boston Art Club, September, 1936.

50 ZAŌ GONGEN
Eleventh century
Bronze plaque; H. 8¼ in. (21 cm.)

The Metropolitan Museum of Art; Rogers Fund

Zaō is shown with a three-pronged thunderbolt in a manner similar to that in No. 48 above, except that here the design is engraved with strong outlines. This flame-shaped plaque from the Kimpuzen Sutra Mound may have been set into a pedestal, either as an independent icon or as the halo for another piece. *Illus. p. 99.*

Published: *Kimpuzen*, Pl. 41, p. 103.

51 ZAŌ GONGEN
Twelfth century
Hollow-cast bronze; H. 10⅜ in. (26.3 cm.)
Anonymous loan

Similar in iconography to Nos. 48–50 above, this small, free-standing bronze is simple and ingenuous in spirit. The garments have been deftly modeled and a surface decoration of incised circles appears at the hemline; traces of gilding remain. Bronze figurines similar to this have been found in the Sutra Mound of Kimpuzen-ji, the temple which served as the main sanctuary of the deity (*Kimpuzen*, Pls. 32–34). *Illus. p. 100.*

52 SUE WARE BOTTLE
Ninth–tenth century
Grey pottery with ash glaze; H. 8 in. (20.3 cm.)
Howard Hollis, New York

From the fifth century through the tenth the main type of utilitarian pottery in Japan was the so-called *Sue* ware. Derived originally from southern Korean prototypes, these earthenware vessels were usually made on a wheel and baked at a very high temperature. Over 2,000 kiln sites for the making of Sue ware have been discovered, many of them low, tunnel-like structures five feet in diameter, rising up the slopes of low hillocks. Wood ash from the burning fires, falling on the vessels, produced a pleasant, random glaze, and at some sites the potters purposely induced this effect.

On this bottle, the ash fell onto the neck and shoulders, adding color to the pale grey body. The only other decorative touches are two incised lines on the neck, and bands on the shoulder where parallel lines were gently scraped into the clay. *Illus. p. 101.*

53   COVERED JAR
    Ninth century
    Grey pottery with ash glaze; H. 8¼ in. (21 cm.)
    University of Indiana Art Gallery, Bloomington

The influence of Nara period pottery is clearly present in the shape and proportion of this handsome covered jar, but the glaze is the simple ash type favored in the early Heian period. Strangely, ceramics did not fit into the pattern of Heian period estheticism. For all the brilliant innovations in technical processes and esthetic standards which took place in metalwork, lacquer ware, and paper making, the ceramics industry tended to become more and more conservative and devoted to simple utilitarian purposes. Even the three-color and deep green glazes which were known in the Nara period were gradually abandoned. Perhaps the diminished contacts with the Chinese mainland shut off the sources of stimulation or influence. Whatever the cause, the great affinity the Japanese showed for ceramics in their later history did not begin to manifest itself again until the closing years of the Heian epoch. *Illus. p. 102.*

54   SUE WARE JAR
    Ninth–tenth century
    Pottery with ash glaze; H. 8¹⁵⁄₁₆ in. (22.7 cm.)
    Capt. and Mrs. Roger Gerry, Roslyn

The brownish-green glaze on this jar is distributed in a random, accidental manner. The solid shape and thick walls give a sense of the simple utilitarian beauty of early Heian ware. *Illus. p. 102.*

Published: *Japanese Ceramics from the Collection of Captain and Mrs. Roger Gerry*, Brooklyn Museum, 1961, No. 12.

55   ROOF TILE
    Late eighth century
    Grey clay; diam. 7¼ in. (18.4 cm.)
    Peabody Museum, Salem; Gift of C. G. Weld

This lotus design, boldly confident and realized with fluent plasticity, reveals the strong influence of T'ang Chinese decorative arts, which appears even in such a subsidiary art form as this. Tiles of this type were made in the Nara

area from the mid-eighth century onward; some identical with this one, which is said to come from Murō-ji, were recently excavated at the site of the Dining Hall of Kōfuku-ji (*Kōfuku-ji Jiki-dō Site*, Nara, 1959, Pl. 21.1). If the present tile is indeed from Murō-ji, then the early affiliation of this remote mountain sanctuary with Kōfuku-ji is further demonstrated. *Illus. p. 103.*

56   ROOF TILE
    Early Heian period
    Grey clay; diam. 7¼ in. (18.4 cm.)
    Peabody Museum, Salem

In contrast to the previous example, the lotus pattern of this roof tile from Kōfuku-ji is less plastic in conception and is arranged in a more linear and two-dimensional manner. Here the T'ang influence is no longer so apparent. For a similar example from Kōfuku-ji, see K. Iwai, *Kokawara Shūei*, Nara, 1936, Pl. 29, No. 147. *Illus. p. 103.*

57   ROOF TILE
    Late twelfth century
    Grey clay; diam. 11 in. (28 cm.)
    Peabody Museum, Salem; Gift of Howard Mansfield

This tile was probably made for the rebuilding of the Daibutsu-den hall of Tōdai-ji after the destructive fires set by the forces of the Taira clan in 1180. It is inscribed with the names of both Tōdai-ji and the Daibutsu-den, and in the center is the Sanskrit character *A*, the "seed letter" for Dainichi according to Esoteric Buddhist thought.

The reconstruction of this building, the ancient symbol of the unity of the Empire and the grandeur of the faith, required some fifteen years and an immense expenditure of effort. The work was supervised by the monk Shunjōbō Chōgen and assisted in part by the Retired Emperor Goshirakawa and the military government in Kamakura. On its completion in 1195, the dedication ceremony was attended by the new feudal ruler of Japan, Minamoto no Yoritomo. Although this tile may have been conceived during the waning moments of the Heian period, it is an emblem of the new artistic and political order of the Kamakura period; aesthetically it is clear and didactic, devoid of grace or subtlety. *Illus. p. 104.*

Glossary*

Aizen—An Esoteric Buddhist deity; one of the Myō-ō (*q.v.*), he symbolizes the theological concept that human passions and illusions are identical with enlightenment. This is expressed in his Sanskrit name, Rāgarāja, King of Passion.

Akshobhya—"The Imperturbable"; one of the Five Wisdom Buddhas (*q.v.*), he was thought to dwell in his own Pure Land in the East. During the Nara Period, he was the object of considerable popular devotion as the lord of mercy for the sick and for the homeless ghosts of the dead.

Amida (Amitābha)—One of the most devoutly worshipped deities in Sino-Japanese Buddhism, Amida is the Buddha who reigns in the Western Paradise. As the personification of eternal life, boundless light, vast compassion, he will welcome to Paradise those who, with a sincere heart, call out his name.

Amida-dō—A temple hall dedicated to the worship of Amida and furnished chiefly with images of that deity and his attendant Bodhisattvas, Kannon and Seishi.

Amida Raikō—The approach close to earth of Amida and his attendants to receive the soul of a dying believer and to welcome him to Paradise.

Avalokiteśvara—*See* Kannon.

Benzai-ten—The Indian deity, Sarasvatī, believed to be the source of language and letters, music and eloquence. Widely worshipped in India today, her cult came to Japan together with that of the goddess Kichijō-ten (*q.v.*) as part of the popular Buddhism of the eighth century. Interestingly, both goddesses were gradually admitted into the pantheon of Shinto, or native Japanese, deities.

Bishamon-ten—Chief of the Four Deva Kings (Shitennō, *q.v.*) whose statues are often installed as guardians of an altar or temple. Known in Sanskrit as Vaiśravana and also as Kubera, he originated as an ancient Indian folk god, Lord of Wealth, ruler of the Yakshas (*q.v.*) and Regent of the Northern Quadrant. He became a popular deity in Japan, and the object of an independent cult.

Biwa—A lute-like musical instrument brought to Japan from the Asian mainland. One of the two basic types originated in Iran, one in India.

Bodhisattva—*See* Bosatsu.

Bosatsu—A class of Buddhist deities extolled in Mahāyāna literature, for they labor unceasingly for the benefit of mankind. Among the major Bodhisattvas, only Miroku (*q.v.*) was related to an historical person; the rest were embodiments of theological and spiritual principles such as compassion, grace, divine wisdom, or steadfastness. In theory, the Bodhisattvas possess the wisdom and power necessary to enter Nirvāna (*q.v.*) but refrain from doing so in order to assist others to reach Salvation. *See also* Kannon, Jizō, Fugen.

Buddha—*See* Nyorai.

Daibutsu—"Great Buddha"; an ancient designation for the giant bronze statue of Dainichi (*q.v.*) at Tōdai-ji.

*Literal translations are placed in quotation marks.

Daibutsu-den—The hall which encloses a Daibutsu.

Dainichi Nyorai—The supreme deity of Esoteric Buddhism and its forerunners; symbol of the great generative force which lies at the heart of all creation, the origin of all other Buddhas, all states of being. Called Mahāvairocana in Sanskrit. *See also* Ichijikinrin.

Enmei Fugen—*See* Fugen.

Esoteric Buddhism—*See* Mikkyō, Tantrism.

Five Wisdom Buddhas—The Gochi Nyorai, the five Tathāgatas placed in the center of the Kongōkai mandala (*q.v.*) symbolizing the five types of wisdom which lead to supreme enlightenment. In their center is Dainichi (*q.v.*), and they include Amitābha-Amitayus (*see* Amida) and Akshobhya (*q.v.*).

Four Deva Kings—*See* Shitennō.

Fudō—"The Immovable"; perhaps the most prominent of the Myō-ō (*q.v.*). Fudō symbolizes, among other things, fearlessness and steadfastness in the face of passion and temptation.

Fugen Bosatsu—The Bodhisattva of all-pervading goodness, the special patron of believers in the Lotus Sūtra (*Hokke-kyō, q.v.*). In Buddhist imagery he is often shown mounted on an elephant. A special Esoteric form of this deity is the Fugen Enmei, "the life prolonging," in which he holds Tantric thunderbolt emblems and is sometimes given twelve arms.

Fujiwara—An ancient and powerful family of courtiers who, beginning in the mid-seventh century with Fujiwara Kamatari, usually at-tained high power in the civil government and distinction in the arts. With the careers of Korechika (974–1010), Michinaga (966–1027), and Yorimichi (922–1074), Fujiwara political and economic fortunes reached a height from which they fell in the latter part of the eleventh century, never again to be fully restored.

Genji-Monogatari—A long novel of 54 chapters written over possibly a twenty-year period ending ca. 1022 by Murasaki Shikibu, Lady-in-Waiting to Akiko, chief consort to the Emperor Ichijō and daughter of Fujiwara Michinaga. While a semi-fictional account of the romances of the Heian court, its hero Prince Genji seems to be modeled in part on both Michinaga and his nephew Korechika. It was widely read by the Heian courtiers, and frequently illustrated in handscroll form.

Goma—The ancient Indian Homa ritual of burnt offerings. Adapted by Esoteric Buddhists as a symbolic means of burning away passions and illusion and other obstacles to Enlightenment, it was performed in Japanese Mikkyō (*q.v.*) temples as a blazing ceremony employing inscribed slats of wood.

Gōzanze—"Destroyer of the Three Worlds"; one of the wrathful Myō-ō (*q.v.*). The name is also borne by the Hindu god Śiva (*q.v.*), who usually appears with his consort Uma beneath Gōzanze's feet, symbolic thus of the supremacy of Buddhism.

Hannya—"The perfection of wisdom"; Prajñā-pāramitā in Sanskrit, the key term in the title of a series of religious philosophical texts produced in India during the first four centuries of the Christian Era and which are among the most important sources of Mahāyāna theology.

Hiragana—*See* Kana

Hokke-kyō—The so-called Lotus Sūtra (*Saddharma-pundarīka,* "*Lotus of the True Law*"); one of the most influential works of Mahāyāna literature and one of the bases of the cult of Amida. Originating in India in probably the first century A.D., this complex text extolls the idea that anyone who has heard the preaching of a Buddha may attain supreme Enlightenment himself. Those who are reborn in any of the Buddhist Paradises are thus given access to a teaching Buddha and the opportunity to attain final release from the bondage of existence.

Hōō-dō—"Phoenix Hall"; a popular name given to the celebrated Amida-dō of the Byōdō-in at Uji, southeast of Kyoto.

Ichijikinrin (buchō)— A form of Dainichi (*q.v.*) symbolizing the wisdom and generative power concentrated in three of the most significant Buddhist emblems: the seed-mantra *bhrūm* (*see* Shūji), the extra-cranial chamber on the heads of the Buddhas (*ushnisha*), and the golden Wheel of the Law. Hence his formal name in Sanskrit is the *Ekaksharoshnishacakra*.

Ishana-ten—An Esoteric Buddhist deity, essentially the Hindu god Śiva in a transmuted form, reduced to the role of one of twelve protective deities of Indian origin (Jūni-ten) whose powers are invoked in Shingon rituals.

Jizō—One of the most prominent Bodhisattvas in popular Mahāyāna Buddhism. Called Kshiti-garbha ("Earth Womb") in Sanskrit, he is the embodiment of compassion and service to mankind, the guardian of children and protector of travelers and warriors; he intervenes in Hell for the sake of those suffering there.

Jōdo—"Pure Land"; a term used in reference to the numerous Paradises in Mahāyāna theology. The one most commonly prayed for, however, is that of Amida in the West, which was thought to be divided into nine separate levels in order to receive the souls of men of different degrees of virtue.

Jūni Shinshō—The Twelve Divine Generals who attend the Buddha Yakushi (*q.v.*), helping him to enforce his twelve-fold vow of compassion to aid mankind and cure it of physical and spiritual ills.

Jūni-ten—Twelve gods of Indian origin. *See* Ishana-ten.

Kana—The Japanese syllabaries; two systems of alphabetic writing made up of simplified forms of Chinese characters to represent the sounds of spoken Japanese. Inspired and guided perhaps by the model of the Sanskrit alphabet, *Katakana* (the angular or straight-line form) is said to have been devised in the eighth century, and the *Hiragana* (the cursive form) in the ninth.

Kannon—The most widely worshipped of all Bodhisattvas in Japan and virtually the archetype of this class of deity (*see* Bosatsu). Kannon is the embodiment of divine compassion, and has limitless power and skill in order to work for the salvation of men. Called Avalokiteśvara in Sanskrit, the deity appears in as many as thirty-three guises—as one of the two attendant Bodhisattvas of Amida, for example; as the Thousand-armed, all-powerful saviour; as the Nyoirin Kannon, possessor of the jewel and wheel which give power to attain any goal; or in the Eleven-headed guise.

Kichijō-ten—The Japanese form of the popular Indian goddess of beauty, good fortune, and wealth, Śrī Lakshmī. Similar in nature to Benzai-ten (*q.v.*).

Kirigane—"Cut gold"; a technique of cutting thin gold leaf into decorative patterns and applying it to a painting or statue; the result is a linear pattern far more delicate and richer in surface effect than that produced by painted gold.

Kōdō—"Lecture Hall"; one of the basic parts of early Japanese temples; a hall for the ceremonial reading of sutras, sermons, and other gatherings of monks.

Kōmoku-ten—One of the Shitennō (*q.v.*); he is the Regent of the West, ruler of serpents and other demonic beings.

Kondō—"Golden Hall"; a standard part of early Japanese temple compounds housing images of the deities most sacred to the place.

Kongōkai (Vajradhātu)—"The ingredient of the thunderbolt." In Esoteric Buddhist speculation, this was one of the ingredients out of which the entire creation was formed, the other being the Taizōkai (*q.v.*). The Kongōkai is roughly equivalent to the Platonic *phenomenon*, or to material existence, to human knowledge, to contingency, to the first step by which human consciousness returns to its divine matrix through Buddhist Enlightenment.

Kongō-shō (Vajra)—A thunderbolt originating in Indian mythology as the weapon of Indra, Vedic lord of rainfall. The vajra became a common feature in Buddhist arts, but in Esoteric Buddhism (which is sometimes called the Thunderbolt Vehicle), it became a symbol of fundamental importance. It is the emblem of Esoteric doctrine that cleaves the darkness of ignorance as lightning pierces the clouds. The wisdom of the vajra is also likened to a diamond as a material that is indestructible, irresistible, and of infinite value. Vajras appear in a great variety of shapes and are sometimes added to bells.

Kōyasan—"Mount Kōya." *See* Shingon.

Kyō (Sutra)—A class of Buddhist texts said to be the record of the original words of Śākyamuni or else the product of supernatural revelation.

Lotus Sūtra—*See Hokke-kyō.*

Mahāvairocana—*See* Dainichi.

Mahāyāna—"Great Vehicle"; the second of three main historic and doctrinal divisions of the Buddhist faith, the first being the "Small Vehicle," or Hīnayāna, and the third being Esoteric Buddhism (Mikkyō, *q.v.*). Mahāyāna doctrines seem to have been formulated in India as early as the first century B.C. and, in part, stressed that the paths of salvation were open to laymen as well as monks, that salvation could be achieved through the assistance of a pantheon of powerful, compassionate deities.

Maitreya—*See* Miroku.

Maki-e—Lacquering technique developed in the Heian period; gold, silver, and copper powder and flakes were set into the lacquer ground or else modeled in designs on boxes, furniture, etc.

Mandala—A theological diagram or schema prominent in Esoteric Buddhism, such as the Kongōkai (*q.v.*) and Taizō-kai (*q.v.*) mandalas. The mandala originated in India, as a highly abstract diagram made up of interlocking triangles and circles, and was used by ascetics as an aid to private meditation. In Japan mandalas are also employed in this way; bearing pictures or other symbols of the deities, they are used in rituals such as baptism and ordination.

Mappō—"End of the Law"; part of the concept that the Buddhist faith must pass through three stages of prosperity and human understanding before vanishing from the earth. It will be revived, and with the teaching of the Buddha of the Future (Miroku, *q.v.*), the cycle of decline will begin once more. Mappō is the third, degenerate stage in which the doctrine is still alive but men are unable to attain enlightenment through their own understanding and power.

Marici—An Esoteric Buddhist deity derived from the mother of the Sun God in Brahmanic Indian mythology. In Japan she was often invoked as protectress against violence and peril, especially by warriors.

Mikkyō—Esoteric Buddhism; the third of the three major historical forms of Buddhism, after Hīnayāna and Mahāyāna. It is also called Tantric or Vajrayāna Buddhism. It developed in the sixth century A.D. as part of an extremely complex, religio-philosophic movement which embraced Indians of all creeds, and it injected into Buddhism a number of magical cult practices, as though to induce the state of spiritual enlightenment through the manipulation of occult forces. While present in Japan in the eighth century, Esoterism in its fullest, most complete form was introduced in the early ninth century by Kūkai and Saichō.

Minamoto—The name (which may also be read Genji) held by several families of warriors descended from the Imperial family during the Heian period. One of them, stemming from a son of the Emperor Seiwa, rose to great power in the late twelfth century, bitterly fought with the Tairas, and finally triumphed in 1185 in the battle of Dan-no-Ura. Their leader, Minamoto no Yoritomo, became the military dictator of the nation with headquarters in Kamakura.

Miroku (Maitreya)—The Buddha of the Future. In texts dating as early as the second century A.D., the historical Buddha is quoted as predicting that one of his lesser disciples, a former Brahman named Maitreya, would become the next fully enlightened Buddha. Until that time (in the remote future) Maitreya was to rise to the Tushita Paradise and dwell there in glory as a Bodhisattva.

Myō-ō (Vidyarāja)—Fierce Bodhisattvas, prominent in Esoteric Buddhist symbolism; the manifestation of the Five Wisdom Buddhas' wrath against evil. Although often seen in sets of five, the Myō-ō most commonly depicted in Japan is Fudō (*q.v.*). *See also* Aizen, Gōzanze.

Nāgarāja—"Serpent king"; a class of deity of a very primitive kind which grew from the consciousness of Indian villagers and was accepted into Buddhism—protectors and guardians of the faith. In China, the nāgas were correlated with the dragons of Chinese nature mysticism.

Nembutsu—"Meditation on the Buddha"; the repetition of a prayer formula such as "*Namu Amida Butsu*" ("Homage to Amitābha Buddha"); the prime act of faith demanded of the followers of the Pure Land creeds in Japan.

Nikkō—"The luster of the sun"; one of two Bodhisattvas who accompany the Buddha Yakushi (*q.v.*).

Ninnō-kyō—"*Sūtra of the Benevolent Kings*," a text of Indian origin which explains how the well-being of a state could be enhanced by the worship of the great, divine guardian kings. The text was read during ceremonies in the Lecture Hall of Tōji intended to promote the safety of the Empire.

Nirvāna—One of the terms used to denote the spiritual state which is the ultimate human attainment in the Buddhist world. The Sanskrit *nirvāna* implies extinction or blowing out (as of a flame), the annihilation of passion and sentiency, the escape of man from the chain of birth and rebirth, the dissolution of the elements of his ego or individuality. While referring to the Enlightenment of Śākyamuni, the term is also used in reference to his death.

Nyorai—The class of fully Enlightened Buddhas who are totally identified with the metaphysical basis of all truth and existence. Called Tathāgatas in Sanskrit, those most commonly seen in Japanese art are Shaka (Śākyamuni), Yakushi (Bhaishajyaguru), Amida (Amitābha), and Dainichi (Mahāvairocana). Iconographically the Nyorai are shown dressed in monastic robes without jewels or ornaments, but there are exceptions to this in Esoteric imagery.

Pure Land—*See* Jōdo.

Raikō—*See* Amida Raikō.

Śākyamuni—"Sage of the Śākya clan"; the historical founder of the Buddhist faith. Born into a princely family ruling in the Nepalese foothills around 560 B.C., his career as a religious leader was centered in eastern and central India until his death in about 480. Among his many titles is "the Buddha" ("Enlightened," or "Awakened"). *See also* Nyorai.

Shaka—*See* Śākyamuni.

Shingon—"True word"; one of two major sects of Esoteric Buddhism in Japan, the other being Tendai (*q.v.*). The sect was established in Japan by the monk Kūkai, with its headquarters atop Mt. Kōya, a remote and isolated spot in Wakayama prefecture. Other major Shingon temples include Jingo-ji near Kyoto, Tōji within the city proper, Kanshin-ji in Osaka prefecture, and Murō-ji in Nara prefecture.

Shitennō—The Four Deva Kings; ancient Indian gods of the four cardinal points of the compass and rulers of the vast host of animistic deities still worshipped by Indian villagers (*see* Yaksha). Depicted in early Buddhist arts as devotees and protectors of Śākyamuni, their imagery became increasingly prominent in China and Japan. *See also* Bishamon-ten, Kōmoku-ten, Zōchō-ten.

Shōgun—Military rank equivalent to general.

Shō Kannon—One of the variant forms of Kannon (*q.v.*); images of the Ārya ("saintly") type stress the physical charm and beauty of the deity.

Shūji—"Seed name"; usually a Sanskrit character which symbolizes an individual Esoteric Buddhist deity; more than a simple initial, each letter is thought to be imbued with something of the force or power of the deity itself.

Śiva—One of the supreme gods of modern Hinduism. The rise of his cult to great popularity in India coincided with the development in Esoteric Buddhism there, and a number of deities and theological notions of the latter are strongly colored by Śaivism. *See also* Gōzanze, Myō-ō, Ishana-ten.

Stupa—The Sanskrit name for the Buddhist pagoda; originating in India as a solid hemispherical mound with a sacred relic placed at the summit, the Stupa form gradually became increasingly more vertical, developing into the tower-like form which prevails in East Asia.

Sumi—Ink used in Sino-Japanese painting; ordinarily made in the form of pressed, dried black pigment (burnt ivory, lamp-black, etc.) which is ground by the artist on a small palette and mixed with water to the desired degree of blackness.

Sutra—*See* Kyō.

Sutra Mounds—Deposits of holy texts (sutras), images and altar equipment interred in the ground to be preserved until the coming of Miroku (*q.v.*), Buddha of the Future.

Taira—One of the great warrior families of the Heian period; it is also called the Heike. The Tairas came to the height of power in the lifetime of Kiyomori (1118–1181), who became the supreme secular authority of the Empire. In the protracted wars with the Minamoto clan (*q.v.*), the power of the Heike was finally broken at the battle of Dan-no-Ura in 1185.

Taizōkai—"The ingredient of the womb"; in Esoteric Buddhist speculation, one of the ingredients out of which the entire creation was formed, the other being the Kongōkai (*q.v.*). The Taizōkai is roughly equivalent to the Platonic noumenon, or innate existence, the first cause, the original step by which the divine ground of existence is converted into matter.

Tantrism—A complex religious and philosophic movement born in India in the sixth century A.D. and which spread widely throughout those parts of Asia adhering to Buddhist and Hindu creeds. Among its many facets was the belief that ritual and magical means could bring salvation to a devotee and the fulfilment of his wishes, in contrast to the emphasis on ethical behavior and asceticism in the more conservative doctrines. *See also* Esoteric Buddhism, Mikkyō.

Tathāgata—*See* Nyorai.

Tendai—One of the two major sects of Esoteric Buddhism in Japan, the other being Shingon (*q.v.*). Tendai, however, originated in China long before the rise of Esoterism, and was an effort to systematize and harmonize all Mahāyāna teachings. When strong waves of Tantric Buddhism from India reached China in the T'ang period, they too were absorbed into the Tendai creed. Saichō established the sect in Japan, with headquarters atop Hieizan near Kyoto. Although Esoteric elements predominate in the atmosphere of Japanese Tendai temples, Pure Land and even Zen Buddhist doctrines were taught there.

Thousand-armed Kannon—*See* Kannon.

Twelve Divine Generals—*See* Jūni Shinshō.

Vajra—*See* Kongō-shō.

Yakshas—Animistic male deities originally worshipped by Indian villagers as guardians of fields and rivers, givers of safety and wealth. Absorbed into the Buddhist pantheon, Yakshas appear widely in the arts of China and Japan. *See also* Bishamon-ten, Shitennō.

Yakushi—The Buddha who heals all ailments, spiritual as well as physical. Yakushi became one of the most popular deities in early Japanese Buddhism at a time when immediate and practical benefits were expected from the faith. *See also* Jūni Shinshō, Nikkō, Nyorai.

Zaō Gongen— The chief of the animistic Shinto gods of Mount Kimpu in the Yoshino district. In keeping with the harmonization of Shinto and Buddhist creeds, he was treated as the incarnation of Buddhist deities and given a guise similar to that of the Myō-ō (*q.v.*), energetic and fiery in spirit.

Zen—A major form of Buddhism which came into prominence in Japan during the thirteenth century; stressing personal self-discipline through meditation, its success was in some ways a reaction against the elaborate rituals of Esoterism and the devotee's passive reliance on the saving grace of Amida in the Pure Land creeds.

Zōchō-ten—One of the Shitennō (*q.v.*); the Regent of the Southern Quadrant.

Bibliography

Akiyama, Terukazu. *Heian Jidai Sezoku-ga no Kenkyū (Secular Painting in Early Medieval Japan)*. Tokyo, 1964. In Japanese, with French summary.

———. *Japanese Painting*. Lausanne, 1961.

de Bary, William Theodore (ed.). *Sources of Japanese Tradition*. New York, 1958.

Buhot, Jean. *Histoire des arts de Japon*. Vol. I. Paris, 1949.

Coates, Harper H., and Ishizuka, Ryugaku. *Honen, the Buddhist Saint*. Kyoto, 1949.

Eliot, Charles. *Japanese Buddhism*. London, 1935.

Keene, Donald (ed.). *Anthology of Japanese Literature*. New York, 1955.

Morris, Ivan. *The World of the Shining Prince*. New York, 1964.

Munsterberg, Hugo. *The Arts of Japan*. Tokyo and Rutland, Vt., 1957.

Noma, Seiroku. *The Arts of Japan, Ancient and Medieval*. Tokyo, 1966.

The Pageant of Japanese Art. 6 vols. Ed. by staff members of the Tokyo National Museum. De luxe edition: Tokyo, 1952; popular edition: Tokyo and Rutland, Vt., 1958.

Paine, Robert T., and Soper, Alexander C. *The Art and Architecture of Japan*. Baltimore, 1960.

Papinot, Edmond. *Historical and Geographical Dictionary of Japan*. Yokohama, n.d.

Sansom, George. *A History of Japan to 1334*. London, 1958.

———. *Japan, a Short Cultural History*. New York, 1943.

Soper, Alexander C. *The Evolution of Buddhist Architecture in Japan*. Princeton, 1942.

———. "The Rise of Yamato-e," *Art Bulletin*, No. XXIV (December, 1942).

Yashiro, Yukio (ed.). *Art Treasures of Japan*. 2 vols. Tokyo, 1960.

Warner, Langdon. *The Enduring Art of Japan*. Cambridge, Mass., 1952.

Catalogue designed and edited by Virginia Field, Assistant Director, Asia House Gallery
Line drawings on pages 92, 97, 99, and the line drawings of No. 55 by Liff Hansen Bernstein.
Color photographs: Nos. 1A and 1B, courtesy of Mainichi Newspaper Company, Tokyo;
No. 5, Barney Burstein; No. 11, Richard Godfrey; No. 15, John J. McQuade;
No. 37A, courtesy of Kyūryūdo Company, Tokyo.
Composition by Clarke & Way, Inc., New York City.
Produced by John Weatherhill, Inc., Tokyo.